TOWARD THE YEAR 2018

TOWARD THE YEAR 2018

Edited by the
Foreign Policy Association

Published by
Cowles Education Corporation,
Look Building, 488 Madison Avenue,
New York, N.Y. 10022

CONTENTS

INTRODUCTION

by Emmanuel G. Mesthene

The chapters in this volume aim to set the technological context of social and international policy over the next fifty years. They should prove widely useful as considered statements by acknowledged experts about the expected states of their respective technical arts.

In tone, the chapters cover the spectrum from optimism to pessimism. Herman Kahn — unwarrantably accounted a Cassandra by some — and Anthony J. Wiener see fewer surprises, fewer wars, greater worldwide affluence, and a more balanced international scene in the next fifty years than in the last fifty. Charles A. Scarlott sees abundant energy, from old and new sources, to serve the world's needs indefinitely, and D. Gale Johnson counters a typical alarum by predicting a general improvement in the world supply of food — and from traditional sources at that.

On the other hand, the depths of pessimism are struck by Philip M. Hauser, writing on population: "Given the present outlook, only the faithful who believe in miracles from heaven, the optimistic who anticipate superwonders from science, the parochial fortunate who think they can continue to exist on islands of affluence in a sea of world poverty, and the naive who anticipate nothing can look to the future with equanimity."

Between the extremes lie Anthony G. Oettinger, whose optimistic vision of education technology is tempered by the cold water of human fallibility, and D. G. Brennan, who draws us a picture of Armageddon and manages to keep his balance in the end only by hoping that peace

Emmanuel G. Mesthene is Executive Director of the Harvard University Program on Technology and Society. He has served as a consultant to the White House on science and technology.

may once more become fashionable. In this connection, Gordon J. F. MacDonald says, "I find it difficult to imagine any major weapons system that is truly space-based." One hopes these do not turn out to be famous last words that are denied even their fame for want of anyone left to ascribe it to them.

The concatenation of the several chapters points up an interesting difference between a number of modern technologies whose influence on the future will be important and a smaller number that will, in addition, be spectacular. Given population growth, major advances will be needed in food and energy technologies, for example, to maintain a dynamic status quo. This will also be the case with military technology, whose continued development is a condition of *maintaining* the international balance of power, and with the transportation technologies discussed by Najeeb E. Halaby, which we'll need to keep up with growth in the numbers and mobility of people.

Space, weather, communication, and information technologies, by contrast emerge as the motors of *change* in the next fifty years. (So does what Ithiel de Sola Pool calls behavioral technology, although one is somehow more convinced by the arguments for the harder technologies.) We discern the new and unfamiliar in the papers by MacDonald, Thomas F. Malone, J. R. Pierce, and Charles R. DeCarlo, which is what gives computers, satellites, and transistors their spectacular aura. The more traditional technologies will either advance and maintain an already familiar present condition or they will fail to advance and induce a sort of "negative" or "backward" change to equally familiar antecedent conditions, such as poverty, starvation, or conquest. But if the new technologies advance as predicted, they will bring about "positive" changes — that is, genuine novelty, along with the uncertainties and unfamiliarity that novelty implies for national and international policy.

Those of us who are professionally engaged in discerning the effects of technological change on society find that our attention begins to focus on a number of pervasive and long-term trends that seem to be characteristic consequences of contemporary technology. Among these are rises in economic productivity, a decline in individual privacy and the consequent enhancement of public issues and concerns, a growth in the social importance of information and knowledge and an inclination toward rationality in decision-making, and institutional changes in the direction of a crossing and interpenetration of functions and responsibilities.

INTRODUCTION

It is noteworthy that these themes recur frequently also in the following chapters, which were written in connection with the fiftieth anniversary of the Foreign Policy Association and which are therefore concerned more specifically with the effects of technological change on international relations. Both Kahn and Pool predict continued economic growth for all the nations of the world, although they take opposite positions on whether the gap between rich and poor will increase or decrease as a result. Just as technology alters the relationship of citizen to government, so will communication and intelligence technologies reduce the possibility of national privacy, according to MacDonald, and thus alter the relationships of government to government. DeCarlo displays the opportunities for greater rationality in international affairs that are potential in the advance of information technology, and Pool and Oettinger, finally, suggest that significant institutional changes will be needed if these and other opportunities are not to be stillborn.

These authors are concerned principally with tools and with the possibilities and opportunities that tools open up. It remains for diplomacy and for social policy generally to determine whether wisdom will infuse the use of those tools. They may not, even with knowledge of the tools. They certainly will not without that knowledge. Therein lies the value of this volume.

CHAPTER 1

WEAPONRY

Disintegrator Rays Likely Will Be "Conventional" Weapons, But Warfare Possibly Will Be Bloodless

by D. G. Brennan

Perhaps the most striking characteristic of modern civilization is not its technology, though that is certainly striking enough, but the rate at which that technology is changing. "Old" ways of doing things vanish, and new ones appear, in small fractions of a human generation. Discussing technology fifty years from now is thus something of a risky business.

Because military technology draws on many fields of sub-technology, and is additionally dependent on non-technical influences mentioned below, it is one of the fields least subject to long-range forecasts. To provide some perspective on this problem, it will be useful to begin with some past forecasts.

Looking Backward

Let us first go back one hundred years and ask how well someone writing in 1868 could have predicted the military technology of 1918, at about the end of World War I. There is an amusing and instructive historical example written in 1878 by Friedrich Engels:

D. G. Brennan, a mathematician and expert in national security problems, is a member of the Hudson Institute. He is also editor of the new international journal, Arms Control and Disarmament Annual Review.

The Franco-Prussian War [1870-1871] marked a turning point which was of entirely new significance. In the first place the weapons used have reached such a stage of perfection that further progress which would have any revolutionizing influence is no longer possible. Once armies have guns which can hit a battalion at any range at which it can be distinguished, and rifles which are equally effective for hitting individual men, while loading them takes less time than aiming, then all further improvements are more or less unimportant for field warfare. The era of evolution is therefore, in essentials, closed in this direction.[1]

Of course, Engels did not write this as a prediction for a specific point in time forty years later, but we may so interpret it. Developments of "revolutionizing influence" that were extant by 1918, but which were not foreseen by Engels, include the beginnings of the military use of aircraft, the tank, the machine gun, chemical (poison-gas) warfare, motor-driven land transport (trucks and ambulances, for example) for the relatively rapid movement of men and supplies, and the beginnings of radio communication. I am tempted to add the armored surface warship and the submarine; although Engels ostensibly was concerned with "field warfare," these developments were of substantial indirect importance even for this purpose.

Engels was not very imaginative, or thorough in surveying possibilities. A competent professional writing about these matters in 1878 — if any existed — should have noticed the Gatling gun used in the American Civil War and observed that its potential future development did not augur well for the continuation of traditional European infantry tactics. And the ironclad ships "Monitor" and "Merrimac" (among others) should have foreshadowed some of the developments in armored surface warships. But no mere professional in 1878 could have foreseen the airplane or radio communication, and it would be asking quite a lot to insist that one should have invented the tank, the submarine, and chemical warfare.

Looking Toward 1968

Let us next consider how well someone writing in 1918 could have predicted the military technology available fifty years later in 1968. It would have been easy to have foreseen considerable development in the use of

2

aircraft, although many early writers on aviation underestimated developments by a factor of ten (an "order of magnitude," as technical people would often put it) or more, sometimes much more. Our hypothetical analyst writing in 1918 would almost surely have predicted a much greater role for chemical warfare than we think of it having today — but this only illustrates the point (which I shall elaborate below) that technology is often dominated by fashions in warfare.

A good analyst might have speculated about such possibilities as vertical-takeoff aircraft or naval aircraft carriers, but probably without getting in the right ball park as to scale — for example, of the helicopters in use in Vietnam or the nuclear-powered supercarriers of the "Enterprise" class. The list of developments even the best man would likely have missed for 1968 is lengthy: jet engines, radar, inertial guidance of missiles and aircraft, pilotless air-breathing ("cruise") missiles of various types, rocket-propelled missiles of many types (including ballistic missiles that can reach any point on earth within some few tens of minutes), recoilless rifles, the nuclear-powered submarine, the missile-launching submarine (especially with underwater launch), the use of large-scale electronic data-processing computers in major military command and control systems (as in the SAGE air-defense system), the use of artificial satellites in orbit about the earth for such purposes as reconnaissance and communication, and — above all — nuclear weapons. Indeed, a detailed study of future technology conducted under high-level government auspices in 1937 missed each and every one of these developments, all of which were in use or under development within the following ten to twenty years.[2]

The reader will deduce that I am not optimistic about the prospects for producing a sharp characterization of the military technology of 2018. This history should serve as a reminder that, although we can extrapolate some of the lines of development that will evolve from current technology, we are likely to miss some of the interesting combinations of such things. And although we may try to guess a few of the developments or inventions that will not just be extrapolations, we are most unlikely to guess right on many.

The job is harder now that it was in 1868 or in 1918 because we have institutionalized the process of innovation itself. The United States alone supports a research and development program in military technology on the order of $7 billion per year. Things therefore change faster. On the other hand, more people now pay attention to predictions and there is more practice in making them, so we may be acquiring more competence in projecting the future. Although some things in this chapter may seem amusing to a reader in 2018, and the omissions will be spectacular, the chapter is very unlikely to look as silly as Engels' statement looked as early as 1918.

There are two major sources of influence on the evolution of weaponry that are not technical in nature. The first of these has to do with fashions; the second with prevailing trends and "temperatures" in international diplomacy.

Fashions in Weaponry

It is not widely recognized, but nevertheless true, that fashions — that is, a rough prevailing consensus on admissible kinds and uses of warfare based on much-less-than-detailed analysis of all possible alternatives — are very important in shaping modes of warfare. The fact that something is merely fashionable does not necessarily make it bad; it may be bad, but it may also turn out — fortuitously — to be useful. For example, it has been unfashionable for many decades to use lethal poison gases in warfare; the propaganda about the inhumanity of gas warfare in World War I is probably responsible. It now turns out that some modern lethal gases are more humane — by such reasonable criteria as minimizing the pain of the victims or minimizing the number of cripples among the survivors — than a number of weapons that are not at all unfashionable, such as mortars, which cut people up in nasty ways. Nevertheless, I should say that, for reasons that would take us too far afield here, the bias against the use of lethal gases is valuable and should be preserved, if possible.

Some fashions are ambiguous or negative in their effects. For example, it became standard doctrine in the United States in the 1950's to rely for security against Soviet attack on the threat of destroying a large fraction of the Soviet economy and population — that is, on deterrence by something like "massive retaliation." There was no apparent technical alternative in the 1950's or early 1960's, so it was not then merely a "fashion." But after 1966 it began to appear that active defense against attack by ballistic missiles could achieve a degree of effectiveness not previously foreseen. The United States and the Soviet Union are thus presented with a choice of the relative emphasis to be given to deterrence on the one hand, or active defense on the other, in their strategic nuclear forces. Some students of strategy have argued that the fashion (as it is now appropriate to call it) of relying on a large number of Soviet "hostages" has become so ingrained in the American Establishment that permitting any reduction in what is called "assured-destruction" capability is not tolerable, and therefore it is not acceptable to shift strategic emphasis toward defense and away from deterrence. This was essentially the position of former Defense Secretary Robert S. McNamara. Others, including myself and many of the principal American academic strategists, believe that this fashion is unwise and that both we and the Soviets would be better served by shifting considerable emphasis to defense.

We cannot take up the details of this controversy here.[3] However, the fact that the controversy exists should illustrate that it would be rash to predict so basic a matter as the relative emphasis placed on deterrence and defense in the strategic nuclear forces of the late 1970's, to say nothing of the year 2018 — quite apart from the fact that the effectiveness of the technologies involved may change in unpredictable directions and degrees.

It would be easy to give many more examples showing that fashions are of fundamental importance. But, no less than as with fashions in dress or entertainment, those in military technology cannot be predicted. All we can do is point to their importance and their changeability, and deal thereafter primarily with the technology itself.

The Link With Diplomacy

The other major non-technical source of influence on the evolution of weaponry is better known and requires much less discussion: National armaments are linked to international relations in general and to international security arrangements in particular. Although most simplistic statements about this, such as "weapons are a result and not a cause of international tensions," are partly false, they are also partly true. For example, the interest in developing weapons in Israel and the Arab states in 1968 is quite different in degree than that in Finland and Sweden. I shall assume in what follows that the world continues for the next fifty years to be primarily one of individual nation-states, each relying to a degree on some combination of national weapons and alliances for its national security, and relying in no substantial degree on international security arrangements. This is not the world I would vote for, but it is the one I believe is most likely. Of course, other possible worlds might also be compatible with the weaponry and problems I shall discuss, but some possible worlds would not be.

In the following section I shall describe some potential developments in relatively basic technology. Next, I shall indicate how some of these technological developments might appear in military applications. Finally, I shall discuss how some of these developments and applications may interact with international diplomacy. It should be clear that I am making no attempt to exhaust the subject.

Exciting Advances In Sight

Materials: One of the newest fields of technology, and one of the most exciting, is that of materials science. It is also a field that is key to many potential military applications, ranging from deep-diving submarines to high-efficiency jet engines (resulting from turbine blades able to withstand higher temperatures). Although the field of metallurgy is perhaps a hundred years old, it is only since about 1930 that systematic attempts have been made to treat the structural properties of materials as a science and, concomitantly, to synthesize materials with prescribed properties. Inasmuch as the field has begun to burgeon only since about 1950, it seems possible that it is only in its infancy and is due for great strides analogous to those occurring in electronics in the last two decades. If so, it will have a revolutionary impact on more areas of military technology than we can enumerate here. I shall touch on some of the more important cases below.

It is also possible that advanced materials will have a major impact on civilian applications, though this is less certain; 1968 costs of exotic structural materials range up to $100 per pound or more. At present, it is mainly expensive missions in space and vital military applications that can effect a major saving by the use of these materials. If costs come down sharply as the field progresses, which is very likely, civilian applications will increase correspondingly.

The properties being developed are increased strength per unit weight or density, impact strength, high-temperature resistance, stiffness, and so forth. There has been considerable development of high-strength materials made by embedding thin filaments of substances — especially boron, carbon, and glass — in a matrix. It appears that the inherent strength of many materials, including steel and glass, is about an order of magnitude above that of contemporary steel, and this strength may be realized in

6

practice. It is possible that glass may become a (possibly cheap) structural material of general importance.

Weather Control: Quite a lot of attention was paid to fundamental investigation in meteorology in the 1950's and 1960's, much of it with the aim in view of ultimately providing some degree of control over the weather. As of the mid-1960's, many meteorologists seemed skeptical of achieving major breakthroughs at any very early date. But 2018 is not an "early date" as technological advances are reckoned. There is a good chance of major achievements within the next fifty years. If they occur, they might well have some military applications, as discussed below.

Gravity Control: In marked contrast to weather research, very little attention has been paid to the possibilities of direct control of gravity, as opposed to aerodynamic means of lift or rocket propulsion. Indeed, the very term "gravity control" tends to evoke images of crackpots and perpetual-motion machines, and there is no reason whatever for believing that interesting control of gravitational effects will be achieved by 2018. Yet there is no good reason to disbelieve it, either. The civilian motivation to control gravity is overwhelming — a "nice" system would, for instance, do wonders for the urban transport problem — and there is some tendency for society to invent what it needs. There is a chance I may see the year 2018 myself, and if so, I shall not be surprised if on my ninety-second birthday I am able to go for a ride in an antigravity car — though I certainly do not *expect* this. If it happens, there will certainly be military uses.

It may be worth pointing out that, whether gravity control is achieved by 2018 or not, there are certain to be *many* developments by then that would seem about as fantastic to us in 1968 as does gravity control. In that sense, it may be fair to describe antigravity machines as a "typical" development of 2018.

Nuclear Weapons: This is not a subject well adapted to public discussion, but it may be useful to point out that nuclear weapons will probably not get very much more powerful (in large sizes) than they are at present. A standard measure of the efficiency of nuclear weapons is the energy yield per unit weight, generally specified in kilotons per pound (kilotons refer to energy released that is measured in units of thousands of tons of TNT equivalent). It was estimated by Ralph Lapp in 1960[4] that large nuclear weapons (in the multimegaton range) had by then achieved 2KT/pound. Since the theoretical yield limits of the nuclear reactions involved in current weapons are all known, and lie mainly in the range 9 KT/pound to 26 KT/pound, it is not possible for the yield per unit weight to increase very much as long as bombs are confined chiefly to these reactions, which is likely to be for a long time. Thus 5 or 10 KT/pound may be realizable, 15 KT/pound is conceivable, but certainly not much more can be obtained from reactions now in use.

Other reactions are possible in principle, but are not thought feasible by physicists. The extreme case would be the complete conversion of matter to energy according to the Einstein equation $E = mc^2$, which would yield 9 MT/pound. It is unlikely that this would even be approached, but if it were, it is worth noting that this would be "only" about a thousand times as powerful as current nuclear weapons. Because current weapons already have a few *million* times the energy yield per unit weight of TNT, the change to matter-annihilation bombs would seem small in comparison to the change already experienced.

It is likely that the main developments in nuclear weapons for the major powers between 1968 and 2018 will be in directions such as improving the efficiency of small and lightweight weapons, the making of very small weapons, the achievement of specific weapon effects, and so forth. These may well be important, but they will not likely have as much impact as some of the other developments we are considering. A more important possibility, from the perspective of this chapter, is that very cheap and simple weapons may be devised that will be easy to fabricate by even the least developed of countries, or perhaps by dissident groups or even gangsters. The implications of this possibility will be taken up later.

Electrical Power Sources: Many items of military interest, ranging from flashlights to spacecraft in orbit, have been limited in their performance by the availability of compact sources of electrical power. This problem has been satisfactorily solved for the nuclear submarine. Elsewhere, however, developments have not yet been very impressive. There is no known reason why batteries or other power sources should not be very much better than they are today. For example, good contemporary batteries will provide 10 watts per pound for a one-day (10^5-second) mission or, in terms of energy storage, 10^6 joules per pound (a joule is one watt-second). In contrast, thermonuclear weapons with a yield of 2 KT/pound yield 10^{13} joules/pound — seven orders of magnitude above the batteries. It is most unlikely that transportable power sources will be achieved that will yield the same energy density for controlled electrical release as the energy density of high-efficiency thermonuclear bombs, but let us be wildly optimistic and ask for something, say, of two orders of magnitude less, or 10^{11} joules/pound. This is, for example, one megawatt-day per pound, which if achieved by 2018, especially in small sizes, would make possible *many* interesting military (and civil) applications.

Chemical Warfare: The fact that this field is unfashionable has kept research programs from being heavily funded, and has kept away many scientists of the first rank. Even so, the technical progress achieved since World War II is reported to be substantial. This indicates that if chemical warfare research ever does become fashionable and heavily supported, the technical progress (at least of the great powers) might well be astronomical. If so, I would guess that the most interesting developments might not be in lethal anti-personnel agents, but rather in non-lethal, anti-personnel weapons and perhaps in still other directions, such as defoliating agents or others that alter the environment in non-lethal ways. Chemical warfare is perhaps more likely to become popular only among small states, which would use older and less sophisticated agents.

Electronics: The developments that have occurred in electronics in the last 15 years are scarcely plausible even to those who have been closely associated with them. The most striking advances have been in the area of solid-state devices such as the transistor and its offspring, the microelectronic integrated circuit, in which many transistor-like devices are fabricated together with their interconnections on a single "chip," using optical and other manufacturing techniques to reduce the components to incredibly tiny dimensions. A single chip perhaps 80-thousandths of an inch square — that is, about 1/12 of an inch square — and a few thousandths thick may, with today's technology, contain 500 active elements (by comparison, a representative large and complicated television receiver may contain 50 active elements). The size of current microelectronic equipment is dominated by the problem of interconnecting the chips. If one extrapolates the trend of the last decade to the year 2018 in a straightforward way, one would expect to find computers with a capacity on the general order of the human brain (but much faster) that could be carried in a shoe box, or perhaps in one's pocket. There will be *many* military applications of such technology.

Lasers: I think it was in 1956 that I heard a distinguished scientist, whose principal research field was physical optics, say that physicists had about become convinced that a coherent source of light would never be possible to achieve. The laser, which is exactly such a source, was invented in 1958, and the first operating model was achieved in 1960. By 1962, people were modulating laser beams for communication and bouncing laser beams off the moon. The laser provides a uniquely concentrated source of radiant energy; for example, it can already provide an intrinsic brightness about eight orders of magnitude greater than that of the sun. Many military applications of this device are already under consideration or development, such as target illumination and tracking, target destruction, radar, and communication. Infrared laser radar using holographic techniques will provide three-dimensional spatial information, which will constitute a major "breakthrough" in radar performance for both civil and military applications. (These techniques may also work with microwave radar.) It seems quite safe to predict that the laser will be one of the principal items of military hardware in 2018, most especially if suitable compact energy-storage devices, such as small devices providing a megawatt-day per pound, can be achieved.

Hypersonic Aircraft: Contemporary aircraft can operate at speeds up to about Mach 3, or about three times the speed of sound in air. (The speed of sound in air is about 740 miles per hour at sea level.) Within the next decade or two it will probably be feasible to develop aircraft that will go to Mach 10 or Mach 20, at least at high altitudes. Whether this development will actually be realized is less clear. Propulsion for aircraft in the Mach-15 speed range is likely to come from supersonic-combustion ramjets, called "scramjets." (A ramjet is a jet engine without a mechanical compressor stage, the compression being provided by "ramming" the air into the engine intake by the forward motion of the engine at high speeds. Something else must be used for starting the motion.) This mode of propulsion may be feasible to Mach 25 or more; the feasible limits are likely to be dominated by materials developments, in this case for skin materials of high-temperature resistance and for engine materials. However, cooling techniques may serve as a partial substitute for developments in materials.

If anyone wants them, aircraft capable of orbital speeds — Mach 25 — or more within the atmosphere may be technically feasible well before the end of the century, and where this technology will go by the year 2018 is anyone's guess. (A plane traveling Mach 25 in the lower atmosphere would be spectacular to behold and — especially — to hear. Indeed, the acoustic shock wave might constitute a significant weapon effect for limited purposes.) There is more likelihood of interest in military vehicles at such speeds at high altitudes, such as in an application discussed below.

Sea and Space Are Future Battlegrounds

Having considered some possible developments in basic or relatively basic technology, let us now take up a few possible applications to military systems.

Weather Control: If significant control of weather is achieved, it may well have major military applications, though these will depend to a great extent on the nature of the control achieved and on what other military technology prevails. For example, naval planners have often thought of sending a hurricane against another side's fleet. It might happen that by the time it is feasible to send off hurricanes on demand, surface naval vessels will play a very small military role; or it might happen that surface vessels will be able to travel at 100 knots or more (using a captured-air-bubble technique or similar means), and be able to outrun hurricanes very handily. Similarly, for attempting to pin down enemy aircraft with storms, the aircraft may well prove capable of all-weather operation. But it is unlikely that all significant military operations by the year 2018 will be independent of weather, and to the extent that they are not, they may be susceptible to interference effected by means of weather control. However, it should be noted that weather control as a military technique is one that is quite likely to be inhibited by considerations of international diplomacy, as will be discussed below.

Deep Submergence: It is probable that materials developments in the coming years will make possible submarines with a depth capability of 20,000 feet or more. This would make almost all of the ocean floor accessible to submarines and submarine-supported technology. (Of course, vessels even now can get to ocean depths of 20,000 feet or more, but they are not pressure hulls that can float with their own buoyancy.) Some students of naval warfare, notably Dr. John P. Craven, believe that control of the ocean depths affected by such technology will dominate anti-submarine warfare in future years. Thus it is possible to envisage deep underwater "fortifications," fences, weapon centers, and so forth.[5] It is also possible to envisage considerable diplomatic controversy about such uses of the seabed, as I shall indicate below.

Guidance: It is not clear whether one should count guidance a "basic technology" or a "military application." I have included it here because it cuts across so many fields of sub-technology, such as materials, but admittedly the choice is somewhat arbitrary. In any event, guidance performance in the year 2018 is almost certain to be limited much more by what people choose to develop than by what is basically feasible. It will literally be possible to put an intercontinental ballistic missile down a smokestack from a range of 6,000 miles, if anyone wants to do it. This would require some form of terminal guidance to compensate for unpredictable atmospheric fluctuations. Using only conventional inertial guidance — that is, accelerometers (based mainly on gyroscopes) that sense movement — and using such guidance only during the boost phase of the missile, it will probably be possible to reduce guidance errors at intercontinental ranges to 100 feet or less, provided the earth is mapped with sufficient accuracy. (Indeed, the earth might be "mapped" most accurately in wartime by observing the point of impact of the first missiles fired.) Using any of several possible means, it will be possible to position aircraft with as much precision as people wish to pay for; indeed, the technology required is already essentially available. Planes can thus be recovered by a fog-enshrouded carrier or directed to prescribed targets in an enemy zone.

Aerospace Plane: Several advanced aircraft and space system concepts have been combined in the concept of an aerospace plane, under study since the early 1960's. (An earlier device of this kind called "Dyna-Soar" was under development beginning about 1958 and was cancelled about 1962.) Such a craft would take off from an airfield, using some form of air-breathing propulsion and aerodynamic airlift, and fly higher and faster until it was in orbit. The system in its initial configuration would probably employ two or more stages, analogous to multiple-stage rockets, in which the first stage would contain the propulsion and part of the airlift required for initial launch, and would return to the launching airfield. Later stages would be smaller and more efficient for high-altitude or orbital cruise operation. Vehicles of this type are of potential interest for a number of military missions, such as bombardment and reconnaissance; however, their overall importance is by no means well established. If the technology is actually developed, it could be operational in the 1970's. Therefore by the year 2018, it is quite likely that there will be many types of aerospace vehicles capable of military operations that will similarly blur the distinction between air space and outer space. These systems will have important interactions with international diplomacy, as we shall see.

Antigravity Belts: If a suitable form of gravity control can be achieved, one of the most interesting applications would be to individual lifting devices for individual soldiers. Even if the antigravity mechanism did not itself provide horizontal propulsion, relatively modest sources of thrust could easily be provided. A cheap form of such three-dimensional mobility for individual infantrymen would revolutionize the tactics of land warfare, which would then probably resemble 1968 tactics even less than the helicopter-borne assault wave in Vietnam resembles the trench warfare of World War I.

Rocket Belts: Even if antigravity belts are not achieved, there are other possibilities. Millions of moviegoers have seen James Bond fly through the air with the aid of a rocket-propulsion mechanism strapped to his back, and other millions saw or knew of similar exhibitions at the New York World's Fair in 1964-65. These devices were based on the limited propulsive capability of back-carried, chemically powered rockets, which are good for no more than a minute or so of operation. They are, therefore, unlikely to be of much military interest. However, the efficiency with which fuel can be converted to thrust in air-breathing jet engines is very much greater, and there is no theoretical reason why a miniature jet engine could not be developed that could be back-carried together with sufficient fuel to provide thirty minutes of operation or more, assuming the use of chemical fuels only. Achievable limits will probably depend more on materials developments than on any other single factor. I believe it is virtually certain that such technology will be developed, probably well before the year 2018, but it is less obvious that costs will permit every infantryman to be equipped with jet propulsion.

Space Systems: The United States, the Soviet Union, and most other states are parties to the Outer Space Treaty, signed and ratified in 1967. It prohibits the stationing in orbit or in outer space of nuclear or other weapons of mass destruction. It also prohibits military activities on the moon or other celestial bodies. However, many military applications of space systems that do not contravene the treaty may be in use by the year 2018. These include reconnaissance, early-warning systems, command and control of strategic forces, communication systems, satellite interception and inspection, and defensive systems (using non-nuclear weapons) to intercept ballistic missile attacks or components of other types of missile-interception systems. Other military applications will undoubtedly be devised well before the year 2018.

Communication: Since the dawn of warfare, one of the important limitations in its conduct has been in the ability to communicate to, from or within the military forces in the field. As of today, these limitations are rapidly disappearing; they will almost surely have vanished altogether long before the year 2018. The major technical development involved, of course, is the communication satellite. It is already on the ragged edge of feasibility to provide reliable communication to and from not only every ship at sea and every plane in the air, but also to every soldier in the field and from soldier to soldier. Fifty years from now the problem of communicating with military forces will loom about as large as the problem of providing them with the correct time appears in 1968. This will be a new thing in the world.

Disintegrator Rays: Fifteen years ago, or possibly even ten, one might have asked a representative scientist which of the technical devices appearing in the Buck Rogers comic strip was *least* likely to be achieved in the near future. If I am not mistaken, most (certainly I myself) would have pointed to the disintegrator ray gun. It would have been a bad choice, as the invention of the laser in 1958 made apparent. I have already mentioned a number of potential military applications for this device. The most dramatic of these, if it proves as feasible as seems likely, will be its use as a disintegrator ray gun.

There has already been a good deal of study of the possibility of using laser beams to destroy warheads on intercontinental ballistic missiles, but this is a singularly difficult application and it is not clear that all the problems involved can be solved. However, I suspect that there is very little question that field-transportable units can be developed that will rapidly burn holes in tanks, to say nothing of individual soldiers. Thus, the main weapon mounted on tanks of the 2018 era may be not a 120-mm. cannon or a rocket launcher, but a high-powered laser. If so, it will have interesting implications. For example, the first requirement in protecting other tanks will not be several inches of tough steel armor, but a highly reflective mirror-like surface — and the counter-counter weapon will be paint bombs of flat black paint!

There is no apparent fundamental reason why lasers could not be made in small units, suitable for use as individual infantry weapons or sidearms, but full exploitation of this possibility would depend on the development of suitable compact power sources. If, for example, small power sources can be developed that would yield anything like the energy levels discussed earlier (a megawatt-day per pound), it might make possible laser weapons of the general size and weight of a pistol — but of considerably greater potency. It should be noted, however, that sustained megawatt-level beams will not be possible from hand-held devices unless there are equally dramatic advances either in energy conversion efficiency or in cooling techniques! But even beams of a kilowatt or less could be militarily interesting. On balance, it will not be at all surprising if laser weapons largely or wholly supplant pistols and rifles, and perhaps many other conventional types of firearms, by the year 2018.

It should perhaps be mentioned that laser weapons are not the only possibility for advanced small arms. Weapons to propel darts carrying some temporarily incapacitating agent are under current development.

Arms Race Will Tax Diplomats

Several of the developments mentioned above may have important interactions with international diplomacy in the 2018 era. That technical possibilities limit, or at least influence, diplomacy is widely recognized. Less well understood is the fact that the reverse is also true — and of comparable importance.

One recent example of diplomacy limiting technology concerns a communication technique developed by the M.I.T. Lincoln Laboratory in the early 1960's. "Conventional" communication satellites, when used for purposes of military communication, are potentially vulnerable to enemy attack and destruction. In a development program given the rather silly name of Project West Ford (originally designated Project Needles), a space-based communication system that would have been substantially invulnerable to short-term enemy attack was designed and tested. The system entailed placing into orbit a very large number of very tiny dipoles (fine bits of wire, perhaps seven-eighths of an inch long and one-thousandth of an inch or less in diameter), dispersed in such a way as to form a very tenuous but roughly continuous "belt" of dipoles about the earth. A mere 100 pounds of copper could yield a billion dipoles or more.

Project West Ford demonstrated that such a belt could indeed be dispersed in orbit and provide suitable military communication capabilities. Up to 1968, no alternative communication technique was known that would be equally difficult for an enemy to disrupt; indeed, it appears unlikely that such an alternative will be devised. Moreover, the procedure can be carried out in such a way as to create very little interference (and that temporary) with astronomical research. But for reasons we shall not analyze here, many optical and radio astronomers around the world objected strongly to the program, and the objections became a major subject of diplomatic discussion in a number of national and international bodies. As a consequence, there is no plan to deploy such a belt, not even in a crisis, and the system seems as dead as the dodo.

Other examples are better known — though perhaps they are no better recognized for what they are: limitations on military technology imposed by international diplomacy. The "unfashionable" status of lethal anti-personnel gases mentioned earlier is an important case in point. And, of course, much of the substance of arms control consists of such limitations. The partial nuclear-test ban discourages the United States, Britain, and the Soviet Union from developing certain nuclear weapons that might (or might not) otherwise be developed (and the French and Chinese are not at all close to the weapons in question). The Outer Space Treaty prohibits the deployment, though not necessarily the development, of orbital nuclear bombardment systems.

Let us now turn to some of the interactions that may occur between international diplomacy and the developments mentioned in the preceding two sections.

Weather Control: Unless weather control techniques can be reliably implemented with a precision of localization that seems rather unlikely, the international community is likely to take a dim view of any national military application. The wrangle that developed over Project West Ford would be nothing in comparison to the outcry that would ensue from having a man-made hurricane visit some unintended neutral country. Thus, there is at least a large chance that most military applications of weather control would not get past the experimental stage. In any case, the techniques used would most likely be those that have first been fully developed for non-military purposes. However, it remains to be seen what kind of international reception even non-military applications would receive.

Deep-Sea Technology: Military applications of sea-bottom technology — to antisubmarine warfare, for example — are likely to have a large impact on international diplomacy, unless diplomacy heads off the applications before they ever take place. The issue is joined as of 1968, but the outcome is in considerable doubt. The government of Malta has proposed to the United Nations that the seabed be put under international control, and that all non-peaceful uses be proscribed. In a speech to the U.N. on November 1, 1967, Ambassador Arvid Pardo of Malta said:

> Current international law encourages the appropriation of [the ocean floor] by those who have the technical competence to exploit it. . . . The process has already started and will lead to a competitive scramble for sovereign rights over the land underlying the world's seas and oceans, surpassing in magnitude and in its implication last century's colonial scramble for territory in Asia and Africa. The consequences will be very grave: at the very least a dramatic escalation of the arms race and sharply increasing world tensions, caused also by the intolerable injustice that would reserve the . . . resources [of the seabed] for the exclusive benefit of less than a handful of nations. . . . Traditional activities on the high seas would be curtailed and, at the same time, the world would face the growing danger of permanent damage to the marine environment through radioactive and other pollution: this is a virtually inevitable consequence of the present situation. . . .[6]

As a statement of immediate prospects, Mr. Pardo's speech is rather alarmist, but the actual possibilities for conflict in the longer run are real enough to be worth taking seriously. If the doctrine of national ownership of the ocean floor comes to be accepted, especially for military purposes, and if most or all of the seabed is appropriated by individual states, the diplomatic problems generated by the situation will be a noticeable part of the scene in the year 2018.

The Fuzzy Boundaries of Space: It is clearly established international law that air space over individual states is national in character and subject to control by individual states. It is almost as well established that *outer* space is not subject to national control and that satellites, even those with military missions (such as reconnaissance or early-warning) compatible with the Outer Space Treaty, have a presumptive right of overflight. Now, there is a problem here: The Outer Space Treaty does not prescribe, and no other obviously acceptable authority prescribes, just where air space ends and outer space begins. (There is no salient technical criterion, such as a discontinuity in air density.)

This problem is not yet serious only because all flying vehicles that have so far been developed can more or less be clearly defined as aircraft or spacecraft. But ambiguous vehicles are clearly foreseeable, long before fifty years elapse, as in the case of the aerospace plane discussed above. The diplomatic problems engendered by this situation may or may not be adequately solved by the year 2018. A simple and perhaps likely solution, especially if it is adopted relatively soon, would be to take a somewhat arbitrary altitude such as 100 kilometers as the dividing criterion, analogous to the various limits traditional for national waters in the law of the sea. But other, more complicated, perhaps more dynamic and troublesome criteria are conceivable. The evolution of this situation will be interesting to watch.

Unidentified Attacks: Many items of advanced military technology will probably be in the hands of many more nations in the year 2018 than they are today. Several of these items — Polaris-type submarines and the flying counterparts thereof, perhaps orbiting bombardment systems, and possibly unmanned weapon systems (stored in orbit or elsewhere) of a completely new kind (for example, high-powered laser disintegrators) — may be capable of mounting attacks in such a way that the victim could not identify the nation responsible. If this possibility arises, it would certainly have a major impact on international diplomacy. It is not difficult to think of possible circumstances in which an attacking nation might want to hide its identity, although such circumstances will not be common. For example, a government would likely be much more nervous about indulging in outlaw-type behavior, on the model of Hitler in 1938-39, if it knew that any of perhaps thirty or forty states might participate in unidentified retaliation. Thus, even great powers might move with more caution in such a world.

A possibility in a very different direction would be the mischief that states could provoke in a crisis — for example, if nations A and B are on the edge of going to war, nation C could try to push them over the edge by attacking one in such a way as to make it appear that the other is the culprit. This ancient device may well be very feasible indeed with the weapon technology of the year 2018. If so, it will pose a real problem for the diplomacy of the era.

Warfare by Hardware Proxy: For several decades there has been a distinct trend in military systems of the industrialized nations toward substituting hardware for soldiers to the extent permitted by technology and economics. The trend is certain to continue, the only question being to what extent. As an illustration of the extent that is conceivable (though not especially likely), it is possible that warfare, at least between states with a comparable advanced degree of industrialization, might become almost bloodless, with the fighting taking place largely or wholly between automated or remote-controlled mechanisms. One of the favorite domains considered for such warfare is that of outer space. Several writers have suggested that we might come to accept things fighting things in space as a substitute for men fighting men on the ground, the outcome being decided (by tacit, if not explicit, agreement) by whose space weapons proved dominant. (If control of outer space implied control of air space, which is a conceivable possibility, then the battle for control of outer space would be less ritualized than what I am suggesting here. It would be more like traditional battles for control of the sea or the air.)

Primarily, what is involved is a question of fashion, and how far and how fast a fashion may change. Although a switch to bloodless warfare is a bit farther than I expect fashion to change, it is not impossible fifty years from now. Such a development would certainly have major implications for diplomacy. Pre-war or crisis bargaining would be much more influenced by hardware capabilities than is generally the case today, and probably much less influenced by such traditional factors as bluff. There would be much more diplomatic attention paid to hardware in non-crisis periods, both as to quantity and technical characteristics, than has been common in the 1950's and 1960's. To the extent that this fashion became firmly established, so that warfare seemed very unlikely to lapse into more destructive forms, it might encourage a greater willingness to resort to war. But the fashion might well never seem to be that reliably established.

The Spread of Nuclear Weapons: This subject has itself become so fashionable that it seems unnecessary to say very much about it, although without question it poses one of the most important problems foreseeable on the international scene. There is some connection between the technology of the weapons on the one hand, and the extent to which they pervade the international scene and dominate diplomacy on the other. If weapons come to be so simple and cheap they can virtually be made in basements by crackpots or gangsters, then virtually every nation in the world will have them. I think it very unlikely that international diplomacy would rise to this occasion until after it had blown up, so it is fortunate that nuclear-bomb technology is unlikely to become quite that available. Primarily as a consequence of nuclear-power programs, nuclear weapons are likely to become much cheaper for most nations than they have been in the past, but not so much so that governments will slide into a weapon program by inadvertence. Thus, for the expectable range of technology, whether, when, how, and how many additional nations will acquire bombs will be dominated by fashion.

This is the most important question of fashion before us. It is technically feasible for any nation with a very modest industrial base — perhaps fifty would qualify — to be producing nuclear weapons of its own in the next decade or two. If most of these candidates do not actually build bombs, it will be primarily because of political and diplomatic considerations, although economic concerns are likely to remain a secondary factor for many countries.

There are opposing tendencies in the world in 1968, and it is not possible to predict with confidence how these political and diplomatic forces will evolve in the future, and still less possible to predict how individual governments will react to them. The behavior of the five nuclear-weapon powers extant in 1968 has made the national ownership of bombs appear desirable, at least in some degree and for certain purposes. On the other hand, the tradition against the use of these weapons has become almost overwhelmingly strong, and a certain degree of obloquy would likely attach to the next nation to initiate a weapon program. As of today, significant diplomatic efforts are being made, especially in the form of a non-proliferation treaty, to discourage further national nuclear-weapon programs. It is not inconceivable that these efforts may substantially succeed, and the year 2018 may find a world with only six, or seven, or eight nuclear-weapon states. It is even possible that there may be no more than five (though not necessarily the five we have today). But I would not be surprised if the efforts fail and we find thirty or more nuclear-weapon states on the scene fifty years hence.

If the weapons do spread widely, there will, of course, be important consequences for international diplomacy. It is likely that most international behavior would exhibit new standards of caution — especially if the tradition against the actual use of nuclear weapons has weakened significantly. On the other hand, the situation would probably lend itself to exploitation by reckless states, a fact that might tempt occasional reckless exploiters. Whether this temptation would be offset by other pressures, such as the caution that might be induced by possibilities of unidentified attacks, or conceivably by the growth of international peace-keeping arrangements, is not at all clear.

Widespread possession of nuclear bombs by secondary states might lead to considerable attention to the possibility of the clandestine emplacement of bombs by saboteurs — what is generally called the "suitcase-bomb problem." For a number of reasons, such bombs are unlikely to seem militarily interesting to the great powers, but nations unable to afford advanced delivery systems may be attracted to them. If they ever do become fashionable, there will be obvious implications for the inspection of international baggage and freight.

A Peace Based on Armed Strength

It is barely possible that a completely new fashion may be in the making: international peace. This is, to be sure, most unlikely. Yet there are some indicators that, optimistically interpreted, may point in this direction. For example, conquest no longer seems profitable, even if otherwise successful. Ideology — with the important exception of nationalism — seems to be a generally diminishing force in the world. I have heard it said — I do not know with what accuracy — that fewer people have been killed in warfare in the last fifteen years than in any other comparable period in modern history. If true, this may reflect the trends and forces at work.

Even if peace is indeed becoming fashionable, the basis for that peace may not obviate interest in military technology for a long time to come. Peace may rest to some degree on deterrence — on threat opposed by counterthreat. Kenneth Boulding has often remarked that threat systems are sick. In a sense, they certainly are — in the sense in which a failure of the stability of the system could result in unprecedented disaster. It is for this reason that I am personally sympathetic to a fundamental overhaul of the world order. But we should recognize that there is another sense in which threat systems are not sick: It will at best take some time and trouble to establish a replacement system, and threat systems may have a lot of vitality for maintaining the peace in the meanwhile.

Therefore I think it would be premature to think that military technology is becoming unfashionable, even if — as we may all hope — peace is itself becoming fashionable. The technologists will continue to invent weapons more radical than most of those suggested here, and they will invent them at a pace that will make the technological revolutions of recent years seem tame and slow. This in itself will pose problems for international diplomacy and peace — and, indeed, will do so if for no other reason than that the changes will outpace our ability to understand them.

Whether international diplomacy will prove adequate to the challenges of its own framework remains very much to be seen. But, as a complement to a lot of hard work on diplomacy, I think we may be permitted a little optimism.

NOTES

1. F. Engels, *Herr Eugen Dühring's Revolution in Science (Anti-Dühring)*, International Publishers, New York, 1939. (Original written in 1878.)
2. *Technological Trends and National Policy*, Report of the Subcommittee on Technology to the National Resources Committee, House Documents Vol. 18, No. 360, 75th Congress, First Session, 1937.
3. D. G. Brennan, "New Thoughts on Missile Defense," *Bulletin of the Atomic Scientists*, Vol. XXIII, No. 6, June, 1967. A more detailed and up-to-date (but less widely available) discussion is given in "Ballistic Missile Defence: Two Views," by D. G. Brennan and Johan J. Holst, *Adelphi Paper No. 43*, The Institute for Strategic Studies, London, November, 1967.
4. Donald G. Brennan and Morton H. Halperin, "Policy Considerations of a Nuclear Test Ban," in Donald G. Brennan, ed., *Arms Control, Disarmament, and National Security*, G. Braziller, New York, 1961, p. 248.
5. John P. Craven, "Sea Power and the Sea Bed," U.S. Naval Institute *Proceedings*, April, 1966, pp. 36-51.
6. *Science*, Vol. 159, January 5, 1968, pp. 66-67.

CHAPTER 2

SPACE

Communication, Weather, and Spy Satellites Create New Problems as They Solve Old Ones

by Gordon J. F. MacDonald

The use of space technology to understand and control our physical environment presents problems of increasingly greater import in the largely unchartered region where the interests of science and foreign policy meet. The first ten years of space exploration have already seen a rapid evolution in the character of the interaction between space activities and international affairs. Even greater changes can be expected as we progress from a tentative exploration of the potential uses of space to an application of space technology to some of the world's most pressing problems.

In examining future applications, it is essential to remember that space technology by itself is of limited use and becomes effective only when coupled with other ground-based technologies. In particular, most of the uses of space technology that I will discuss here will be possible only if satellite systems are closely linked to computers of very much larger capacity than those available at present. The interdependence of space

Gordon J. F. MacDonald is Executive Vice-President of the Institute for Defense Analyses and a consultant to the National Aeronautics and Space Administration. He formerly was a professor of geophysics at the University of California at Los Angeles.

and computer technology to produce new systems will not be an isolated example; complex systems of the future will increasingly depend on broad advances in many areas of technology.

In its early days, the United States space program was considered largely as an instrument for achieving international political objectives. Once technology had produced rockets of sufficient capacity to place scientifically meaningful payloads into orbit, a program of scientific exploration of space would have been a natural step. In fact, however, the size of the U.S. space program was determined not by scientific requirements, but by the implicit recognition that a nation's power and vitality are measured in part by its technological achievements.

The Soviet Union clearly recognized the prestige potential of a successful space program. Ever since the launching of Sputnik I, the Soviets in their public pronouncements have linked their accomplishments in space with Soviet military capability. In addition, the Soviets, appreciating that demonstrations of technological competence have implications far beyond military power, regularly emphasized their very real exploits as proof of how far Marxist policies had taken them in science.

Both the United States and the Soviet Union have clearly accepted the position that a display of a superior technology is one measure of a nation's ability to fulfill its economic and political objectives, as well as to meet its military commitments. The early recognition that a nation's political power is to some extent determined by its ability to compete in major scientific and technological endeavors led both nations to make investments in space that are quite large compared with the immediate needs of science.

In the battle for technological prestige, early accomplishments are highly visible; as the technology matures, further progress does not have such dramatic impact. The advancing atomic-reactor technology brings some measure of prestige to the countries possessing it. However, these advances no longer carry with them the aura of scientific accomplishment that the first detonation of fission or fusion weapons did. In space technology, the first ten years have seen a similar maturing of attitudes. The very great technological capabilities of the two space powers are widely recognized and no foreseeable development is likely to alter materially this general assessment. Thus, although prestige gained from space accomplishments will continue to be an important consideration in evaluating the effect of space activities on international relations, it will not dominate as it did during the early years of the space program.

Although considerations of prestige have influenced the public's view of space, this technology has affected Soviet-U.S. relations in another and perhaps more profound way. It has made possible, at least in part, the realization of President Eisenhower's "open sky" proposal. Although public knowledge of such satellite programs is severely limited by secrecy, it is widely believed that both the major space powers have used space-based platforms to obtain photographic and communications intelligence. Information gathered in this way may have determined to some extent the present pace of the strategic arms race. By providing the defense planners of each nation with data relevant to the changing weapons systems of the other, the satellite intelligence influences deployment decisions. Such information may slow the arms race by reducing uncertainties about the competitor's capabilities; or it may quicken the pace by allowing early recognition of new systems, leading to swift reaction to them. Whatever the capabilities of present information-gathering satellites, future technology will provide systems of such power as to make meaningless the concept of a nation's privacy. I will return to this point — one of utmost importance to the international diplomacy of the future.

U.S.-Soviet Cooperation Possible for Space Exploration

During the early years of the space program, President Kennedy, motivated apparently by his desire for a detente, sought cooperation in space with the Soviet Union. He believed that development of areas of common interest could gradually be expanded as time went by, thus establishing a habit of cooperation between the two countries. Looking ahead to the near future, it is clear that there will be numerous opportunities for new and substantive collaboration with the Soviets.

Some of the early proposals for cooperation involved actual joint physical implementation in space ventures. (For example, President Kennedy, in a speech before the United Nations General Assembly in 1963, suggested that the Soviet Union and the U.S. join in sending to the moon representatives of a number of nations.) The preliminary attempts resulted in limited agreements for sharing meteorological data, examining possible joint efforts in obtaining magnetic data, and in using communications systems. Future cooperation may take a quite different form as a result of pressures placed on the programs of both the Soviet Union and the U.S. by limited resources. The exploration of the planets and the

25

moon, for example, will require commitments of resources that will be large even for the two major space powers. Cooperation between these countries and eventually with other nations might take the form of *planning* for, rather than actual joint physical implementation of, space experiments. Joint planning would permit a maximum use of the non-overlapping resources of the countries involved, while at the same time providing prestige returns to each. Cooperative planning has the additional advantage of not necessarily involving detailed hardware considerations; as a result, problems of security in the narrow military sense are not as relevant as they would be for actual joint implementation of space flights.

For example, the Soviets recently penetrated the atmosphere of Venus with a probe. Although this experiment was not entirely unexpected, U.S. planning for the exploration of Venus had not taken into account possible Soviet results. The experiments aboard the U.S. Mariner V, which flew by Venus shortly after the entry of the Soviet probe, in part confirmed by indirect radio techniques what the Soviets had obtained by in-place observation. We do not know to what extent the Soviet planning for Venus recognized possible U.S. experiments, even though U.S. plans had been published several years earlier.

Duplication of effort may have been valuable during the early stages of space exploration because of the high probability of failure. The great reliability of the present system, resulting from continued experimentation and advances in technology, eliminates the need for repetitive experiments. In the same sense, the rapid development of a broad area of space activities dilutes the prestige value of any particular space success. There is no longer the great prestige advantage that accompanied a scientific discovery made in advance of a competitor. This is so even for exploration of the planets, in which considerations of celestial mechanics permit visits from the earth to a particular planet at intervals spaced as far apart as one to two years. Only if one nation were to completely dominate an area of exploration, such as lunar and planetary studies, would the present balance of space-related prestige be upset.

Considerations of resource allocation, of the limited prestige value of isolated scientific discovery, and the positive values derived from enlarging areas of contact suggest that, in the future, cooperation in planning for the exploration of space will be rewarding to both the Soviets and the United States. Planetary exploration might be the earliest and most suitable candidate for combined planning efforts: Journeys to the planets are expensive, and they require long lead times because of limited opportunities for making the journey and great sophistication in instrumentation if the instruments are to survive the lengthy voyage. Furthermore, planetary investigations have no relevance to problems of national security, nor has any nation made a national goal of planetary exploration.

Space technology today influences relations among nations other than the U.S. and the Soviet Union only obliquely. The U.S. has cooperative arrangements with certain countries and has aided several by providing technological assistance to scientific space programs. Cooperative arrangements exist with a large number of countries with regard to the use of antennas or other fixed facilities, and a number of nations have agreed not to place destructive weapons into space. These developments, however, are peripheral to the basic flow in the relations among nations.

As we proceed from the exploration of space to the widespread use of space technology in support of earth-based endeavors, questions other than those of prestige or limited cooperation assume much greater importance. As we look ahead, it is helpful to consider separately those technologies that are essentially global in character, those that are strongly national, and finally those that affect questions of national security in the broadest sense.

Applications of space technology to problems of communication, navigation, traffic control, weather forecasting, and weather control are examples of what may be called global technologies. Their implementation requires the participation and cooperation of many nations. Although such technologies might be useful to a single, continental-size country like the Soviet Union, their true value rests in worldwide application. At the same time, their development presents a host of problems with regard to operation and regulation, as well as raising the question of the proper forum for airing disputes that might arise.

Communication Satellites

Satellites are already an important adjunct to other means of common-carrier communication. As capability and versatility of satellites increase, I can foresee their application to a much broader field of communication. In the near future, satellites will be used as a relay to convey information from point to point on the earth's surface between increasing numbers of small, inexpensive, mobile and fixed terminals, each having simultaneous or multiple accessibility to the satellite. In time, such systems should replace a majority of the present hard-line communication systems between centers of population, although within any center more conventional means may still be used. The principal problem will be the appropriate use of the limited frequency bands available for communication. As higher electrical powers become available within the satellite, more effective use of the frequencies available at present will be possible. At the same time, other advances in electronics may be expected to widen the bands available by permitting higher frequency electromagnetic waves to be used as carriers of information.

There are significant international consequences of a very greatly enhanced communication capability. In the first place, international organizations must be formed so that agreement can be reached on frequency allocations as well as on rules of use. Today, fifty-four nations, excluding the Soviet Union, are signatories to an agreement establishing a single, global commercial satellite system as part of an improved global communications network. This agreement must be widened to include all nations if the system is to be truly effective.

A further and significant consequence of a global communication system is that it would permit the international use of giant computer complexes. The availability of such computers on a shared-time basis to users throughout the world would have myriad applications to problems of health, education, science, and trade. For example, data banks, maintaining information relevant to all substantial financial transactions, both local and international — and which could be queried at any time — would revolutionize international trade.

A specific application of a linked computer-communication satellite capability lies in the field of traffic control. At the present time, increases in air traffic over the oceans and other unpopulated areas, and advances in operational capabilities of aircraft, have produced navigation and traffic-control problems that are becoming acute, particularly over the North Atlantic. For example, the present separation standard is 120 nautical miles laterally, 20 minutes' flying time longitudinally, and 2,000 feet vertically. These standards, in all probability, will have to be reduced if the anticipated increase in air travel is to be adequately dealt with. A system whereby a beacon on an aircraft relays information by means of a satellite to a computer would permit precise location of the aircraft and enable much greater traffic flow than would be possible by using more conventional techniques. In addition, such precise navigation and traffic control would markedly reduced the adverse effect of weather on operations and greatly aid search and rescue operations.

As with other communication-related space applications, traffic control and navigation require the combined efforts of all nations that use aircraft. The system will be effective only if all planes are under its control. At present, only preliminary steps have been taken toward the implementation of such a system. The Scientific and Technical Subcommittee of the United Nations Committee on the Peaceful Uses of Outer Space has recommended to the parent committee that a working group be established to consider and make recommendations on the need of such a system and to examine some of the legal questions. Actual implementation would require international agreements on the beacons to be used aboard aircraft, the assignment of proper frequencies and broadcast bands, and other technical and operational questions.

Direct-broadcast television satellites may strongly influence the achievement of national goals and indirectly affect international relations. In the United States, network programs are transmitted between cities by common-carrier facilities, and are then broadcast from a large number of high-powered television transmitters. Many important and populous nations have neither the common-carrier network to span the country, nor television transmitters to reach the viewer. Communications satellites may eventually make television available even in developing countries. At present, it is impractical to broadcast directly from a satellite to a standard television receiver — the power required is too large. Indeed, even direct radio-broadcast satellites are beyond the state of the art at present. The direct TV transmitter requires primary power sources considerably beyond the 35-kilowatt capabilities of satellite reactors currently being explored. In addition it requires the development of a large, space-erectible antenna that could be accurately pointed at a particular geographical area. However, such advances could easily be achieved in the next twenty years.

Television and, to a somewhat lesser extent, radio are direct and powerful tools in the hands of a central government. Leaders can appeal directly to the people without distortion or deletion. That this is a powerful technique has been illustrated in the U.S. Presidential elections. Influential as TV communication is in a society already unified, its impact would be far greater in an emerging nation still seeking national unity and effective government. Many of the most populous nations consist of an amalgamation of different cultures. A good example is Nigeria, a nation of more than 50 million people of diversified ethnic backgrounds that established English as the language of its schools. Nationwide television could be of tremendous value as a motivation for learning English, as a way of establishing and maintaining language standards, and as a means of making nationhood meaningful and desirable to the population. Television of this kind would be almost as valuable to more advanced and far more populous nations such as India and China.

Weather Satellites

Satellites will serve the needs of weather forecasting and weather control in two major ways: by providing a platform for the relay of information picked up by ground-based or mobile sensors, and by carrying sensors that actually probe the atmosphere. The latter use was established in 1960, when a weather satellite was sent aloft that for the first time permitted observation of the earth's weather on a global scale within a time frame suitable for meaningful analysis. Up to the present, satellites have relayed primarily information on cloud cover and on the amount of heat radiated from the earth upward into space. In the next few years, advances both in satellite and sensor technology will permit determination of such relevant parameters as temperature, humidity, and wind velocity throughout the atmosphere.

The evolutionary development of space-based meteorological studies will first see extensive use of satellites in the communication role. Balloons, buoys, and isolated ground stations will be queried by central computer facilities through the communication satellites, which most likely will be in synchronous orbit. The data gathered in this fashion, supplemented by coarse-grain information secured by Tyros- and Nimbus-like meteorological satellites, will provide the initial parameters for the computer in its numerical analysis and forecast. The projected values developed by the computer would then be continually compared with observed quantities, and the forecast updated. Communications satellites would then deliver the forecasted weather on a worldwide basis.

Further in the future, observations will no longer be gathered by sensors at the surface or floating in balloons. Instead, sensors carried by satellites will probe the atmosphere from a distance, using the passive radiation from the atmosphere and transmitting energy through the atmosphere. As in the case of queried sensors, the information would be relayed to a central computing facility for analysis. The sensors-at-a-distance system has great advantages. It would be able to obtain information from all parts of the atmosphere and not just those points where the sensor happens to be.

Again, implementation of either of the above systems will require agreement among all nations participating on responsibility for the emplacement of sensors and for the operations of the communication systems. At present, discussions in international agencies such as the World Meteorological Organization are under way to develop a long-range global atmospheric research program. Such a research program would be an essential first step in developing an operational program.

The meteorological systems I have discussed raise the issue of national privacy. Balloons floating over a country might be thought of as reconnaissance instruments, and satellite-sensor systems will indeed have the capability of describing in detail atmospheric conditions over possible competitive nations. The desire of a nation to maintain its privacy may in the long term hamper the development of such worldwide forecasting systems; yet global cooperation is essential if a system is to be effective. A gap in meteorological data for a nation the size of Communist China, for example, would in all likelihood make impossible accurate long-term forecasts for the world as a whole.

The economic benefits of effective long-range forecasting are great. Various groups have estimated that in the U.S. alone about $2 billion could be saved annually by farmers, fuel producers, and public utilities if two-week forecasts were available.

Beyond forecasting lies the problem of weather modification and control. Here again satellite-computer systems are essential. Satellites provide basic data for the atmosphere; computers model atmospheric processes. The effectiveness of various techniques for modification can be tested by comparing the satellite-observed behavior of the statistically irregular atmosphere with the computed behavior of an unmodified model of atmosphere.

A Census of the Earth's Resources

The earth-resource evaluation satellite can provide the less developed nations primarily, but also the more advanced countries, with an important tool in planning economic development. At present, the techniques for remote sensing are sufficiently primitive so that only gross features, such as the amount of snow cover, can be accurately mapped from satellites. In the future, I see techniques for remote multiband sensing developed to such an extent that a satellite could, for any particular area, take an inventory of resources and, in conjunction with the computer, produce a resource map. Capabilities of this kind could also be usefully applied to the management of agricultural resources and near-surface mineral deposits, fisheries, and water resources. Such satellites would also be of value in alleviating the effects of national disasters in remote regions. For example, a satellite sensor could spot a fire in a large forest, and associated weather satellites would quickly determine humidity, direction and speed of the wind, and other relevant variables. The computer could then determine the most efficient way of bringing the fire under control.

Consideration of earth-resource evaluation satellites again presents questions of national privacy. If a developing nation can use the technology to evaluate its own resources, more advanced nations can use it to evaluate the resources of their neighbors and competitors. Detailed evaluation of the wheat crop in Canada by a Communist Chinese satellite could influence China's decisions affecting its own agricultural program for the year. Widespread and detailed information on resources could thus have profound effects on the conduct of international trade as well as on national planning.

Space-Based Electronic Spies and Weaponry

In the past, the influence of science and technology on international relations has been most dramatic in the field of weapons development. Today, space-related weapons systems, such as intercontinental ballistic missiles and the fractional orbiting bombing system, make up a major element of both the Soviet and the U.S. strategic military power. I find it difficult to imagine any major weapons system that is truly space-based. Satellites are inefficient platforms for the launching of weapons, and I see no particular advantage to large space platforms, even if equipped with immensely powerful lasers, because of their vulnerability to even larger ground-based laser systems. Satellites can, of course, play an important supporting role in command, communication, and control because of the enormous flexibility of satellite-communication systems.

The most probable military application of space technology will be in the field of surveillance; satellites will be equipped with a very wide variety of sensors that will supplement photography in a variety of ways. For example, it may be possible to obtain detailed information on the temperature and composition of smoke from a factory chimney or the electric power output of a reactor facility. Thus a nation could be kept informed in detail on the conventional weapons developments of its competitors. Moreover, a modern complex weapons system must be thoroughly tested in the environment. Although attempts can be made to hide or camouflage the tests, it is unlikely that such attempts would be effective against the multisensored satellites of the future. It would thus be possible for any nation to receive substantial advance warning of the deployment of a given weapons system. Furthermore, information on complex systems gathered in this way would permit the design of highly effective countermeasures.

It may be possible for ultrasophisticated satellites to monitor population movements, the number of automobiles and tractors, housing elements, and perhaps even the number of workers in a particular factory at a given time. This wealth of information, coupled with major computer facilities, will allow defense planners to project accurately a nation's total capabilities. Nations would truly be living in the open.

Threat to the Right of National Privacy

One of the most highly prized of a nation's resources is its privacy. Where national sovereignty prevails, a nation can largely control information-gathering within its borders. The potential of satellites for earth-oriented data collection gives rise to challenging questions regarding this valued resource of privacy. Can limits be placed by international law upon satellite data collection and how are these limits to be enforced? Can legal obligations be placed on a nation gathering data to share that information with other nations? What are the consequences of such an open sharing of basic data relating to national activities?

The opportunity for a completely open world provided by technology raises the issue of the dependence of international stability on a degree of national privacy. Is the most stable situation one in which nations essentially possess no secrets? Or would international relations be so upset by widely available information that instability would result? Is there an optimum amount of information that all nations should share?

National response to the development of a technology that can effectively violate national privacy may take one of several forms. There may be a gradual abandonment of the concept of sovereignty with the formation of federations of contiguous states. Such a move would receive impetus from the future development of global technologies such as weather modification and control. An alternative response might be the abandonment of open, large-scale warfare as a means of securing national advantage and the adoption of methods for secret or covert wars.

By the year 2018, technology will make available to the leaders of major nations a variety of techniques for conducting secret warfare, of which only a bare minimum of the security forces need be apprised. One nation may attack a competitor covertly by bacteriological means, thoroughly weakening the population (though with a minimum of fatalities) before taking over with its own overt armed forces. Alternatively, techniques of weather modification could be employed to produce prolonged periods of drought and storm, thereby weakening a nation's capacity and forcing it to accept the demands of a competitor.

There can be no doubt that technology, developing on a global scale, will profoundly alter the classical concepts of the nation-state system. The world's response to such developments will depend to a very substantial extent on a widespread appreciation of the power of the technologies involved. If they are to lead to a more stable world, their long-term effects must be anticipated, because the problems they raise possess a complexity that will make our present concern with nuclear affairs seem simple by comparison.

CHAPTER 3

TRANSPORTATION

Superjets, Superfreighters, Air Trucks, and Rockets Will Further Close the Gap Between Nations

by Najeeb E. Halaby

Transportation, in my view, should be the facility to transport vast numbers of people where they want to go, when they want to go, at a price society can afford. There have been isolated examples of mass transportation in man's history — the migratory tribe following its flocks and herds throughout the seasons is one, and even the tidal ebb and flow of urban commuters today is mass transportation in a bottle. For the most part, however, our efforts to become mobile have lacked both scale and organization. In this respect, almost any colony of ants would put us to shame.

One reason for the random character of our transportation has been the fact that man is not by nature a really mobile animal — at least, so far. Given the choice, he will, like his relatives the great apes, stay fairly close to his home precinct. Unlike those more rudimentary forms, the birds and fishes who wander large areas of the earth, man is essentially a homebody who would rather adapt himself to minor changes in his environment than move to a new one.

Najeeb E. Halaby, former Administrator of the Federal Aviation Agency, is Senior Vice-President of Pan American World Airways.

When these changes become too drastic, of course, he must move. The series of ice ages that began perhaps 700,000 years ago forced early man or proto-man to cross the forming deserts and the newly emerged intercontinental bridges and proliferate across the earth.

Can we say proliferate? Were there ten thousand of them? A hundred thousand? Surely they were lonely travelers amidst the alien vastness of our planet. And when they found the secure valley or the hospitable savanna, they settled down for another round of generations, until some natural cataclysm either wiped them out or nudged them on.

Nature Has Anchored Man to His Home

This, in general, is the history of humanity and transportation. Man has always been asking himself if this trip is necessary. And in a way Nature, like a jealous wife, has conspired to tie him to his immediate environment. When man found he could domesticate animals and provide himself with instant food and four legs for transportation (and another's legs, at that), he soon realized that he had to stay around home to take care of a herd.

With the discovery, perhaps 15,000 years ago, that the seeds of a certain grass that we now call wheat could assuage those constant pangs of hunger, man also found that he had to guard his own wild patch of edible grass or cultivate one for himself. He became a farmer, tied to the land.

The man who turned a potter's wheel upright and discovered it could be used to carry burdens was probably the world's first transportation expert. Or perhaps it was the wily fellow who found that if he tied two logs together he could take a friend on a trip down the river.

Although the wheel and the sail, with an assist from the plodding caravan, introduced a measure of organized transportation to the world, the effects of this new mobility were scattered, peripheral, and anything but revolutionary. Indeed, during the first dozen centuries of the Christian era, it seemed at times as though the world was drawing in upon itself. The pre-Copernican earth was flat, and the mist-shrouded horizon formed the boundaries of the average man's world.

The Age of Transportation: Postponed

The great age of exploration transformed this concept of the earth in the minds of the enlightened few, but it did not change the realities of the world for the tribesman, the villager, and for the dweller of the burgeoning, pestilence-ridden cities. For these citizens of the newly minted, round world, reality lay not in the silks of China, but in the corn in the nearby field or the flour from the mill by the stream. Travel and transportation had waved a wand, but their magic effect was still largely unfelt across the globe.

The great age of steam and the machine, the 19th-century Industrial Revolution, should have introduced the age of transportation. But several odd things had happened on the way to the mobility millenium.

In the first place, it turned out that man himself had outpaced his early technology. Ruled by the inexorable ratio that demographers know as the doubling rate — a geometric series that feeds upon itself — the races of man had proved so fecund that the new machine age (and this applies particularly to the transportation machines) never had a chance to catch up with him.

For our original small band of early men had by the end of the 19th century become a swarm numbering a billion and a half souls, and their total was doubling during every seventy-year span. Furthermore, they were a largely immobilized swarm, for probably not more than one in every thousand of them had ever been more than a day's walk from his birthplace. For all but a tiny minority of mankind, the steamship was a fantasy and the railroad a traveler's tall tale.

Another disquieting fact concerning the Industrial Revolution was that the transportation machines it produced — Fulton's steamship, Stephenson's railroad, and even, toward the end of the period, the horseless carriage — turned out to be self-limiting. They were wonders, to be sure, but they were somewhat expensive wonders. Costly to build, hard to maintain, and mechanically inefficient, these energy-eaters provided transportation that often benefited most the cultures that needed it the least. Or, if you want to put it in other terms, 19th-century transportation tended to make the rich more prosperous and the poor more envious.

The Misfit Railroad: Tons to Carry Pounds

The railway is a classic example of a revolutionary form of transport that never quite made the evolutionary grade. In the United States, in certain areas of Western Europe, and, more recently, in Japan, the railroad provided the transportation needed to build an industrial society. Railroads came high. In the United States, for example, railroad construction between 1850 and 1890 absorbed more capital than any other section of the economy. In an expanding and productive economy, this capital returned big dividends; but unfortunately the size of the original investment, as well as the lack of an adequate technology, made rail lines an impossible luxury for vast areas of the world.

The railway in the United States once held the promise of developing into a mass-transportation medium over a wide spectrum of distances. In the course of time, however, it proved to be a mechanical monster that never grew smart enough or agile enough to face the competitive facts of 20th-century life. The result of the competition — some of it from the highway and some from the airway — is a gap that we must some day bridge if we are to have an integrated transportation system.

In terms of people transportation, the railroad is today an evolutionary misfit. It is a brontosauris fighting for survival in a world of jackrabbits and swallows. From the day its tracks are laid, the railroad fights its inherent mechanical inefficiency — its need for tons of rolling stock to carry pounds of passengers, a cumbersome economics, and what might be called a social inflexibility. You must have large numbers of people who want to travel between certain sets of places on fixed schedules to make the railroad an economically practical passenger-carrying medium. The railroad, by its very nature, cannot "do it for cheap."

As a bulk-freight carrier — and we must consider things as well as people in our look at mass transportation — the railroad has a much better record and a more hopeful future. But here again the railroad suffers from its own built-in deficiencies, for it is a short-armed giant that often cannot quite reach either the producer or the consumer of the goods it carries.

As a consequence, the railroad has to live in an unhappy union with its prime competitor, the trucking industry. As if that were not enough, the railroad in the last several decades has had to surrender some of its most profitable trade to the fluid conductor — the pipeline. Today, 70 percent of our energy resources are moving over this nation's million miles of pipeline. Soon this will occur in Europe and elsewhere. Furthermore — and this may be considered a portent of the future — coal has already been moved in a pipeline at approximately one-quarter the cost of its transportation by rail.

Despite its deficiencies and present difficulties, I am sure that the railway, in some form, is here to stay and that it will make a valuable contribution to the transportation "mix" that will characterize tomorrow's society. The rail lines' current dilemma will eventually be solved, it seems to me, by the application of an improved technology and by a kind of social engineering that will fit the railroad's capabilities more closely to each community's needs.

Ships, Wheels — and the Promising Wings

The surface ship, as a transportation medium, is almost an analogue of the railroad. As a freight carrier, it offers the same virtues and disadvantages, and as a people carrier it suffers from the same anachronistic drawbacks as the railway. The proper destinies of the surface ship would seem to lie in carrying bulk cargo and serving as floating resort hotels — providing low-cost freight and high-cost suntans.

This brings me to my penultimate consideration, the motor vehicle. As a regular mode of people transportation, the personal automobile introduces, all around the world, as many problems as it solves. It is inefficient, noxious, and economically incompatible with anything but a spendthrift society. The average 150-pound driver tooling down a million-dollar-a-mile highway, here or abroad, in two tons of expensive and rapidly deteriorating machinery, bound for a destination where it may cost him the price of his day's food to park — this is surely what we mean when we speak of conspicuous consumption.

The fourth of our transportation ways, the airway, is also the youngest and the least exploited. After fifty years of research and development, of trial and error, we have a pretty fair idea of what an airplane can be made to do — though, of course, we are still far from achieving its maximum performance.

We know, for example, that the wing — or airfoil — is the most efficient of all time-rated transportation media. We also know that after four decades of commercial aviation, only one in every four American adults has ever been an air passenger. When you cast the net wider you find that only about 2 percent of the world's population has ever ridden in an aircraft. And of these two groups, many are one-time riders. Yet it is interesting to note that the airlines already account for more public-carrier passenger-miles than the other three forms of transportation combined. From this it is plain that the airplane's great contribution to transportation lies in the future.

More People Going More Places

This brings us to the last third of the "Century of Transportation." I call it this because I believe the wonders we have seen in the first six decades are simply portents of those that will unfold in the final third of this century. The development of both the steam and the gas turbine, the refinement of the internal-combustion engine, the large-scale investment in highway and pipeline, the Wright brothers' leap from the bicycle to the airfoil, and Frank Whittle's surge from prop to pure jet have already established the 20th century as the era of transportation.

What is to come will, I think, further certify this claim. This is also an orderly arrangement, for it leaves the 21st century with the indisputable claim to being the Nuclear Age.

If you are a logical person who seeks for the cause that precedes the effect, you will not have far to look for the sources of our present and our coming transportation revolution. For we are in the presence of several dynamic trends in today's world, and all of them have an immediate and direct relationship to transportation.

The so-called population explosion, which may well double the number of us now on earth by the end of the century, and portends nine or ten billion people by the year 2018, demands a vast increase in man's mobility. As man's numbers mount, he will make increasing demands on integrated systems of transportation to move himself and his goods. Indeed, establishing and maintaining proper distribution channels for food and services may spell the difference between survival and catastrophe on a continental scale.

The manyfold expansion of knowledge and the spread of education now taking place will provide the factual know-how and the trained personnel necessary for the creation and maintenance of new transportation systems. New and more complicated vehicles, sophisticated tools, and new energy sources will demand a wide proliferation of the technical expertise that is now the sole property of a few of the more advanced nations.

The new prosperity — if it is spread and shared among the underdeveloped nations, as it must be — will create a new impetus for travel. The increase in leisure time among the advanced cultures and a widening margin of economic security in the more primitive societies will also add to the ever-growing fraction of mankind that is on the move.

A Revolution in Two Worlds

Finally, what you might call the social revolution — the spreading recognition by man everywhere that he is an integral part of the human family, with a right to a seat at the table — makes mobility, a global mixing of goods and people, inevitable.

The fact that this developing mobility of ours, this transportation revolution, is taking place in two different worlds — the worlds of the haves and the have-nots, of the technologically advanced and the under-developed — presents terrifying problems, but also some interesting possibilities for speeding up developments. Many underdeveloped areas of the world may skip over the long periods and many of the arduous steps that marked the evolution of our own transportation techniques. There is, for example, no use in fussing with a steam-boiler engine if you have available a diesel engine and oil. And many tribesmen who never used the wheel are already familiar with the wing. For it is remarkable and true that an airway can be built at less than 20 percent of the cost and in a fraction of the time necessary for the construction of a railway.

These lacunae in a hop-skip-and-jump development can produce some amusing situations. I recall the case, several years ago, of an American charter plane carrying a load of Iranian pilgrims to Jidda during their pilgrimage to Mecca. At 10,000 feet above the desert, the pilot was startled by the unmistakable odor of wood smoke wafting into the cockpit. He went back to find the pilgrims grouped around a small fire they had built on the cabin floor — heating their tea.

The Problems and Possibilities

Let us look at some of the problems and possibilities that we face in the continuing development of the world's transportation capabilities. We will start with the assumption that any transportation system of the fuure will have to be safe and dependable, rapidly changing and expand-ing to meet demand, economically sound, and technologically efficient. Moreover, all its components will have to be integrated. I am speaking, of course, of technical integration as well as social.

For the transport of bulk cargo, I should think that the ocean freighter, possibly powered by nuclear energy, will share the job with the pipeline in the latter decades of this century. The most economical transportation medium of all for low-value, heavy, durable bulk cargo over long dis-

41

tances would be cargo carriers equipped with flotation gear that could be dumped into the proper ocean current.

For medium- and short-haul freight transportation, I would anticipate that the conventional motor truck, probably powered by a turbine engine, will be around for many years to come. I would be surprised, however, if it did not in the future have its own right-of-way. The mixing of passenger vehicles and large trucks on the public highways is the wildest sort of folly.

Sharing this so-called surface transportation will be a vehicle that you might call "the air truck" — an aircraft that will feature relatively slow speeds with short-range and high-lift capabilities. This, the ugly duckling of the air, would probably be the result of a hybridization of the present flying boxcar and the vertical-lift flying cranes now in use in Vietnam. The virtue of such a solution, of course, is that it combines the efficiency of the wing with a self-maintained, almost unlimited right-of-way.

Regular, scheduled people transportation for distances ranging up to, say, 200 miles will probably be the province of lightweight, high-speed rail lines (such as those now being used in Japan) designed for use in this nation's northeastern megalopolis.

In the field of long-distance people transport, where the airplane will always be preeminent, I believe that we will shortly be producing aircraft that are either as fast as we want or as big as we can use. Note that this is an either-or proposition and that the limiting parameters will be social and economic rather than technological.

Aircraft: How Big and How Fast?

Speed is bought with energy, and energy costs money. Extreme speeds demand excessive energy and certain structural modifications in the airplane. They also introduce a social problem. If we can build an aircraft to transport 125 people from New York to London in 200 minutes at Mach 2, or twice the speed of sound (and more than twice present subsonic jet speed), can we then assume that it would certainly be better to build a Mach 3 airplane and get 250 people there in 150 minutes? Technologically, yes, but not, surely, until we know how much it costs us, financially and socially, to save 50 minutes. In the final analysis, we will have to be guided by what is economically practical, rather than by what is possible, particularly when in ten years we seriously consider the ballistic-missile transport.

The large airplane presents us with even more interesting problems and possibilities. There seems to be no reason why we cannot, in the present state of the art, build an aircraft that will carry, say, 700 to 1,000 people on intercontinental or transcontinental flights at better than present-day jet speeds of 550 miles per hour. With such a capacity, present-day air fares could be reduced to approximately the present level of bus fares per passenger mile — which would add up to less than $100 (in 1967 dollars) for a trip from New York to London. At these rates for a trip one-seventh the way around the earth, the airplane is beginning to look like a mass-transportation vehicle.

The maximum size of our future aircraft (and, as a consequence, the lowest fares for air service) will be dictated by the available passenger pool and our passenger-handling techniques. Will we find ourselves with more seats than there are passengers who want to travel from, say, Bombay to Paris on a given Friday?

Then there is the problem of gearing transportation to existing social patterns. Business travelers who bunch their trips at the beginning and the end of each weekday are faced with the consequent congestion in terminals, both in ground transportation and on the airlines themselves. The coming supersonic transports will bring with them a noise hazard, the sonic boom, that may annoy millions on a cross-country flight. We must find the solutions to problems such as these so that we can reap the benefits of air transportation at an acceptable social cost.

Computerized Travel Documents

There is also a margin of convenience that narrows precipitously as the speed of our transportation increases. When it took a week to cross the ocean, it was not considered too much of an inconvenience to have to stand in line for a few hours to meet the entrance requirements of a foreign country — filling in the customs, immigration, and health forms, and so on. Today and tomorrow, whether we transport 150 people across an ocean in three hours or 800 in six hours, such delays are unacceptable.

Why not, then, computerize travel documents? Under this procedure, every traveler would be provided with a pocket-size plastic card somewhat similar to the credit cards now in use. On this card would be coded all the information necessary for establishing the bona fide identity of the traveler, including his citizenship, health record, previous travel record, vital statistics, and so on. Each major port-of-entry would be provided with links to a computerized "memory" of this information, supplied by the source that issued the card.

Each traveler, as he disembarks at a foreign port-of-entry, would present his card to an inspection official, who would then feed it into a machine that would check it against the stored memory (which might be in a computer center thousands of miles away) and with the requirements appropriate to that port. The machine would immediately indicate whether the card checked with the stored memory and whether the traveler satisfied the entrance requirements. At the same time, entrance charges would be levied against the card's account — these charges to be paid by a central fund that would later levy the appropriate sum against the traveler.

Such an international identity system would establish the traveler as a character-credit risk, with all the relevant information available in microseconds of time. With certain modifications, a similar system could be used to expedite the clearance of the airplane, its mail, and cargo.

I would also expect our traveler's card to carry a set of symbols that would automatically dispatch an arrival notice to the passenger's home. Another communication system would provide every traveler with immediate and continuous contact with the rest of the world while he is in transit. The present relative isolation of the traveler is incongruous; after all, transportation and communication are but two sides of the same coin.

Flying Boxcars Will Carry Anything

The relationship of the future giants of the air to freight transportation is almost too obvious to need underscoring. We are now using jet cargo planes that carry 45 tons of freight at 600 miles per hour for thousands of miles nonstop.

The air-cargo business, which for a few airlines is almost doubling in volume with each year, may be one of our century's greatest growth industries. Pan Am cargo business grew more than 50 percent in 1966 — a little better than the average for the industry as a whole for the previous three years.

The new, giant planes will offer triple the cargo capacity of the present jets and will qualify an entirely new order of freight for the encyclopedic catalog that is already being carried by air. Automobiles, heavy mechanical equipment, seed grains, textiles in bulk, nitrogenous fertilizers, and many other products now carried by surface ship will be transported by aircraft (in 1967 Pan Am supplied Zambia with its necessary fuel by air). Moreover, the speed of this transportation will in many cases obviate costly storage facilities around the world — warehouses will be replaced by an airborne inventory.

One concomitant of the burgeoning air-freight business will undoubtedly be a tremendous advance in the art of containerization. A lightweight, standardized, protective packaging will become a part of every product, and ways will be found to containerize many commodities now shipped in loose or bulk form. Furthermore, the packaging will be designed to fit the demands of all forms of transportation. This will be a part of the evolving integration of the various media of transport and travel.

Converting Miles Into Microseconds

With this background, we can visualize by the year 2018 a world of nearly ten billion people, anyone of whom could fly to its most distant point within eight hours and could conceivably rocket halfway around the planet within an hour.

The superjets, the supersonic jets, the superfreighters, the metroplanes, and the ballistic-missile transports will have made it possible to convert miles into microseconds and oceans into rivers.

Physically, nations would then seem like counties, and continents like states. Peoples and products will be able to move without technical limitations and will be constrained only by economic and social conditions. By means of nearly total mobility, mankind will have achieved what Moses reported in Genesis (I: 26): "And God said . . . let them have dominion over the fish of the sea, and over the fowl of the air, and over the cattle, and over all the earth, and over every creeping thing that creepeth upon the earth."

If, however, futurists such as Herman Kahn and Anthony Wiener are correct, global transportation and communication will intensify two enormous problems. The first will be to meet the demand of a massive population increase. The second will be to help close the widening gap between the haves and the have-nots that will be dramatized by the new technology of the 21st century. [See Chapter 12.] During this period the trend toward urbanization of the world will continue, though I doubt that the rate can be accurately predicted. In any case, there will be more people living in more cities and earning more money with more leisure time for travel. But — more ominously — the gap between the haves and the have-nots will have dramatically widened.

Concurrently, global communication will have developed at a rate as great, or greater, than transportation. Man will not only be able to communicate, but he will also be able to interrogate electronically on a world-wide basis. The concept of secrecy among nations and privacy among groups and individuals will dissolve as communication technology races ahead of society. For most people of the world, the coming of radio and television will stimulate travel, just as the distribution over the past decade of transistor radios to natives in West Africa greatly increased air travel in the region.

What will it all mean? What will society do with the technology?

First, I believe *Time,* with its priceless value to man, can be saved on a universal scale by masses of people who can thereby use it more creatively and productively.

Second, it seems to me that the other most priceless value, *Talent,* can be spread more widely and rapidly, thereby enabling a multiplication of creativity. Because the greatest quality in the world will always be inspired thought and leadership, transportation with communication should facilitate the expansion of human understanding.

Third, psychologically, this new dominion over distance could lead toward a change in attitude about space and time. If there is less "here" and "there," less "we" vs. "they," man will tend to find that "we are all here" — interrelated, interdependent, and thereby compelled to cooperate to survive.

Diplomacy in a World Made Small

These generalizations, if acceptable, clearly have implications for United States foreign policy and diplomacy. If diplomacy, according to Webster, is "the art and practice of conducting negotiations between nations," it is also "artfulness in securing advantages without arousing hostility."

In the world of the early 21st century, the President and the Secretary of State will have even less opportunity than today for secrecy and privacy. At the same time, they will be able to see and hear everything of significance as it happens around the world. Between sunrise and sunset, they will be able to feel the hand and look into the eyes of any other world leader. They will be able to hold an airborne National Security Council meeting traveling at hypersonic speed, with instantaneous communication and nearly universal pictorial display of the current situation of friend or foe. At the same moment, their allies and adversaries will, of course, be equally capable of sensing *them*.

Thus, the whole diplomatic process will inevitably be speeded up, the evidence of capabilities will become more exact, evaluations more accurately quantified, and the scope of intuition narrowed but heightened.

Frightening as this pace sounds, the possibility of major international accidents should be reduced by the better informed, more mobile, and more communicable leadership. In a world where there is more rapid trade in more products, we will have a more interdependent world. And where people and ideas will cross 120 borders constantly, there should be less instability.

However, the compression of distance by transportation and the propagation of information and ideas by communication will dramatically present to all people ugly problems of inequality. The disparity between North and South, between white and colored, between rich and poor, will be starkly before the eyes of all. More people will more readily see the difference between hunger and comfort, health and disease, luxury and subsistence, and the problem for United States foreign policy to bridge these differences will be very great indeed. Regardless of our technology, our foreign policy — and, in an absolute and final sense, our technology, our foreign policy, and our diplomacy abroad will succeed only as we succeed in facing and solving these problems ourselves. And when we arrive in this tiny, supersonic, supersensory world of 2018, there will be only one place left to find the humanity to master the technology — in Man himself.

CHAPTER 4

COMMUNICATION

Face-to-Face Mass Communication Will Become Worldwide

by J. R. Pierce

The international future of communication will be shaped by new resources and new needs. The resources are powerful, the needs are great. The problem of meeting the needs is a considerable challenge.

Yet it would be a mistake to look at the future of communication primarily from the point of view of needs. To an amazing degree, the needs of our technological culture have grown from the exploitation of new technological resources. Many of our present international problems would not exist in a world without modern weaponry, fast transportation, and speedy communication. I propose, then, to turn first to the new potentialities of communication.

Communication technology evolves continually, but today we have entered an era in which change is particularly rapid. This era began with the invention of the transistor by Brattain, Bardeen, and Shockley in 1948. This solid-state era was preceded by two others.

The first was the electromechanical, or electrical, era that followed the first public demonstration of Morse's telegraph in 1844 and the first public demonstration of Bell's telephone in 1876.

J. R. Pierce is Executive Director of the Research Communications Sciences Division of the Bell Telephone Laboratories. An electrical engineer, he wrote Electrons, Waves and Messages; *and* Theory and Design of Electron Beams.

In their early forms, the telegraph and the telephone provided surprisingly sophisticated communication. The telegraph bridged the American continent in 1861. The Atlantic was bridged, falteringly, in 1858 and then successfully in 1866. Telephones soon supplied local service throughout the civilized world, but the extension of telephonic communication over unlimited distances awaited a second revolution.

This came with the second era, the electronic age, which began with the invention of the vacuum tube by Lee De Forest in 1906. The vacuum tube provided the first versatile amplifier. It was through such amplification of electrical signals that telephony was extended across the continent in 1914, experimentally across the ocean in 1915, and commercially across the ocean in 1927. It was the vacuum tube that gave us radio and television. Although Stibitz at the Bell Laboratories and Aiken at Harvard built early electromechanical computers about 1940 without its aid, it was the vacuum tube that ushered in the age of the computer.

The Solid-State Era — An Age Without Limit

The third era in communication is an extension of the electronic age. As I have noted, this new era began with the invention of the transistor. We now have many other solid-state devices, including integrated circuits, or microelectronics.

We are only beginning to experience the truly profound impact of solid-state electronics, which is making available devices that were either impossible or not worth having when vacuum tubes were our only resource. One could make portable radios using vacuum tubes, but they were bulky and the batteries ran down rapidly; the successful portable radio is the child of the transistor. One could, in principle, put complicated circuitry into telephone sets, but the circuitry would have been unreliable and too costly. One could use vacuum tubes experimentally to combine television with telephony, but this process held out little commercial promise. One could make large computers using vacuum tubes, but they were so bulky, slow, unreliable, and expensive that they could never have achieved the widespread use that computers have found in our society. Vacuum-tube repeaters were put on the bottom of the ocean to supply telephonic communication, but the use of transistors increased the communication capability immensely. One could, in principle, also make communication satellites using vacuum tubes, but they would be very poor satellites indeed.

There will be many new advances in solid-state devices as well as ancillary advances in related fields. These will provide us with complicated electronic equipment that will be small, increasingly cheap to make, take little power, and be reliable enough to last for years without attention. We expect that, when complicated solid-state circuits are incorporated into a telephone set, they will be so inexpensive to replace that they will be thrown away rather than repaired when they finally fail.

All this means increased sophistication, flexibility, capability, and economy in whatever type of communication we may use in the future. The sophistication will affect all major aspects of the communication process: the transmission circuits by which messages are carried for short and long distances; the switching systems by which the transmission circuits are made accessible to users, and the station apparatus through which the user delivers or receives the message. Because the last aspect is the closest to the user, I will say something about it first.

New Developments — The World at Your Fingertips

The communication network, national and international, is a powerful resource that can be used indifferently for various human purposes. In this it somewhat resembles the human nervous system; the same kind of nerve impulses carry messages concerning sight, sound, touch, taste, and muscular action around the human body. The sense organs and the brain determine the meaning and utility of these signals. The station set acts as a transducer between electric signals and human needs. The transmission and switching network, like the nerves in our bodies, can serve many human purposes.

In today's world we are still largely limited to the telephone and the teletypewriter (and, of course, to television as mass communication or over special closed circuits). This situation is already changing and it will continue to change profoundly in the future.

A hint of change is found in the appearance of Touch-Tone (a registered trade name) keys on American telephone sets. The importance here goes beyond speed and convenience. Although the signals from a telephone dial are translated at the central office and go no farther, the signals from a Touch-Tone telephone set can go over any talking circuit to any part of the world. Hence, the keys can be used to control distant computers or other machinery after the telephone connection has been established. This is already being done nationally in certain transactions involving banking and purchasing, and it can be extended internationally.

Beyond the limited repertory provided by the 12 keys of the Touch-Tone set, there is a type of keyboard capable of sending letters and other symbols as well as numbers — in other words, a complete text. At present, this is provided by the bulky and relatively expensive teletypewriter. It is clear that solid-state electronics will provide new terminals for handling texts. These will include both smaller and faster keyboards, and smaller, better, and cheaper means for displaying and recording the text. The new terminals will make the transmission and reception of texts almost as convenient and universal as the telephone. Transmission and reception will become a larger part of daily business and diplomacy. Transmission will continue to surmount national boundaries and international barriers such as oceans and deserts.

In the handling of texts, computers will play an important role, which will include editing. After an initial keyboard operation, futher corrections, additions, or deletions will be accomplished without retyping. This will extend even to justification and pagination in the preparation of documents of a quality comparable to today's letterpress. Thus, it will be quicker and easier to generate documents in final form, and it will be possible to transmit these rapidly from place to place.

Although the new resources of electrical communication will break down many barriers, the language barrier is not easily overcome. Some prophets have predicted the early advent of voice-operated devices that will recognize and react to human speech, either to perform various computer or machine functions, or to translate speech or texts instantly into some other language.

Efforts to make computers turn spoken English into written English have run into a very serious block. So have efforts to make computers turn one written language into another. In the human processing of language, understanding plays a central role. When we hear distorted speech, or speech with a pronounced accent, we understand it best if we know what the man is talking about; we ask ourselves what the man might conceivably have said.

Meaning is equally important in translation. I have heard an interpreter with a diplomatic background make hash of a technical or scientific conversation. This was because he didn't understand what he was trying to interpret. In interpretation or translation, an understanding of

51

the subject matter is of an importance comparable to an understanding of the source language.

At present, some workers are trying hard to program into computers an "understanding" of a particular area of human thought or activity. Until this is accomplished, we are unlikely to achieve either a "voice typewriter" or a translating machine of general utility. It may be possible to give a computer an understanding of a limited field of knowledge, but it will be difficult to give it an understanding of all human knowledge. We may have computers that, like some Swiss guides, can talk in English about mountain climbing, but register blank when spoken to about anything else. They may aid people with linguistic problems by providing definitions and glossaries important to special fields. However, they seem unlikely to replace human linguistic abilities, especially in such specialized fields as science.

Speech from computers is more promising. At present, computers can reply to keyboard queries only awkwardly by means of a tape-recorded voice. In the not-too-distant future we may be able to query computers by means of push buttons and get voice replies from texts stored in a memory bank.

Seeing, as well as talking, at a distance is an old idea, but this has become practical only through the solid-state art. The Bell System is committed to the provision of a Picturephone service commercially in the early 1970's. I think that such service will grow rapidly and ultimately become a routine part of an international communication network.

Visual communication may solve many of the problems concerning the display of text and diagrams as well as of the human face and figure. It can augment our ability to control computers and other machines at a distance — and help a physician make a diagnosis though he is half a world distant from his patient. It could have many other uses that at present are difficult to foresee. I do know that visual communication will be easy to add as an adjunct to the communication terminals of the future.

Thus, the communication terminals that businessmen, housewives, and diplomats will use in the future will embody many new potentialities of enormous significance to international relations. It should become possible not only to communicate, but also to confer *meaningfully* with people in any part of the world. And while such a conference is proceeding, it should be possible for each party or group involved to invoke quickly a wide variety of resources, either human or computerized.

What all this will do to the world, I cannot guess. It seems bound to affect us all. If the computer will not immediately solve linguistic problems, communication can encourage intercourse among various peoples. We may expect that more and more people will have a working knowledge of another language, or at least of that part of another language that is of particular concern to them.

Mass Communication — Its Influence Will Grow

The type of communication we have considered so far is directed from individual to individual, from group to group, from person to machine, or from machine to machine. Let us now consider mass communication, which is directed from the few to the many.

Radio broadcasting remains a powerful force in the world. In our nation, television has become even more powerful. The center of our lives need no longer be a distant city; it can be a box in our living room. Television promotes a national image, a national purpose, and a national way of life. Together with radio, television may eventually overcome many regional preferences and many regional peculiarities of speech; at the very least, it will make a uniform grade of speech nationally intelligible.

Already influential, TV is likely to become even more so in the future. Its performance will improve with better color and a sharper picture. Perhaps we will be able to record programs cheaply and replay them later. However, no matter how much television changes, its chief impact will likely remain twofold. First, there will be the broadening of vision, the less parochial attitude toward life, that TV brings. This may be instrumental in creating effective nationhood in developing countries. Second, there will be the encouragement afforded to the international exchange of program materials, either by satellite or by tape. This could bring something of the unity of view and purpose to the entire world that TV is already bringing to nations individually. *Bonanza* and other American TV shows have already demonstrated that the international dissemination of programs is highly practical. What this will do to the world as a whole remains to be seen.

The overwhelming lesson of mass communication is that people will accept it only on their own terms. One cannot do people good by boring them. The opportunity of mass communication is technological. The challenge of television is that of effectively adapting it to human beings, of making it acceptable in whatever context it may be used. Here television differs from the type of person-to-person or group-to-group communication we discussed earlier. Personal communication is controlled by the people involved. They use it to do what they want to do. The human feedback in mass communication is much more indirect. The masses choose, and eventually their voice is heard, but those who generate the programs may be slow to respond. This seems to be particularly true in nations in which programming is controlled by the government.

Station to Station — Miracles in Transmission

We began by discussing communication from the terminal end — the point at which it has an impact on people. We have considered the general types of services that communication will provide to human beings through such terminals. These services are becoming technologically and economically practical, largely through advances in solid-state technology. But terminals themselves are only a part of a communication system, useful only because we have transmission circuits and switching equipment to connect one terminal with another. New and extended uses of communication will be possible only insofar as the real cost of transmission is decreased and the real cost of switching is either kept within reasonable bounds or decreased.

I shall not say much about switching except to point out that the same techniques have been applied to it that are responsible for our rapid advances in electronic computers. We already have electronic switching in commercial operations. The ultimate form it will take is not entirely clear, but I am certain that it will meet new needs flexibly and economically.

In the field of transmission, the revolution that started with the transistor is already working miracles. In local transmission, transistorized repeaters can be placed every mile along a pair of wires in a cable. Originally intended for a voice circuit, the two wires can now handle pulses at the rate of 1.5 million a second. Rates several times this speed will be attained soon, making possible the economic transmission of data, many telephone conversations, or Picturephone signals over existing pairs of wires. A considerable portion of long-distance transmission is by coaxial cables. We can now send 3,600 telephone conversations through one coaxial pipe, or more than 30,000 two-way conversations through a cable containing 20 coaxials.

Ground microwave systems, which beam signals from hilltop tower to hilltop tower, amplifying and then relaying them, provide exceedingly cheap communication over transcontinental distances. Solid-state technology is making microwave systems cheaper and more effective. Furthermore, solid-state microwave repeaters are simple, small, and reliable, as well as inexpensive. Thus, it will be technologically feasible to put microwave repeaters only a few miles apart, making possible the use of higher microwave frequencies. The attenuation or loss caused by rain renders the use of such frequencies impractical with repeater spacings now in common use.

Besides cables and microwaves, we have the potentiality of using extremely high-frequency radio waves to send hundreds of thousands of telephone conversations or thousands of Picturephone signals through buried pipes, or wave-guides, approximately two inches in diameter. This can be done using solid-state devices in the repeaters or amplifiers, without vacuum tubes. Such a system can be built at any time that the traffic warrants. Up to now the total traffic of all kinds between cities has not been great enough to make the use of such a system economically worthwhile.

Further in the future, there is the prospect of communication by extremely high-frequency electromagnetic waves — that is, the coherent light waves produced by lasers. Because of fog and atmospheric irregularities, it appears that such communication would have to be carried by a buried pipe. At present, a pipe capable of transmitting a light signal would be at least as expensive as a wave-guide, so this type of system would be economically justified only for extremely heavy traffic between two points — traffic beyond what now exists. Furthermore, although the band width, or communication capacity, of the light beam is in principle very large, we are not yet able to realize a width substantially greater than that provided by millimeter waves. Laser communication is therefore a resource of the future rather than of the present.

Finally, we come to a very important form of microwave communication: microwave radio using orbiting satellites rather than hilltop towers as relay points. The solid-state electronic art, including the solar cell as a power source, is ideally suited to satellite communication. This art has been effectively exploited in the Telstar satellites and is now in commercial use through the various Intelsat satellites.

The space art has advanced in capability and reliability much more rapidly than many (I, for one) expected. Thus, it is possible to design, build, and launch satellites that would provide far more communication than any we have so far orbited. This could have a profound effect on domestic as well as international communication. At present, the chief obstacles to the further development of satellite communication appear to be organizational and political rather than technological.

Satellites have been proposed for mass as well as personal communication. It will certainly be possible in the near future for a satellite to send signals powerful enough to be received with a relatively inexpensive installation in a city or village. This might be used to bring television to all parts of a nation that does not now have a highly developed communication system — India or China, for example, or even a nation such as Nigeria. Ultimately, it will be technologically feasible to send television signals from a satellite directly to a rooftop antenna, and thus directly into a home TV set.

The use of satellites for television distribution, either to a village or to a home, must be judged on the basis of economy and usefulness. It would be difficult to say that direct satellite broadcasts to homes would give us better television than we now have in the United States. Television by satellite certainly seems ill-adapted for programs of local or regional origin; it is suited best to an all-network service of limited variety. This it might provide very cheaply. The United States already has network television. In the many countries that do not, broadcasting from satellites might have a profound effect, perhaps producing a qualitative difference in national life.

In considering satellite communication, we must always remember the scarcity of radio frequencies. This can be mitigated by calling into use higher and higher frequencies, especially those above 10 gigahertz. Nonetheless, frequencies are limited by nature, while international and national needs for communication appear to know no bounds. We must look toward a day in which all usable frequencies will be crowded. When that happens, it would seem best to reserve radio transmission for those uses to which it is particularly and uniquely adapted, such as communication with ships, airplanes, automobiles, and — in general — people on the move.

Communication between fixed points will become continually less expensive, by cable as well as by radio. Even when we have reached the point of increasing reliance on forms of transmission other than radio, the extension and expansion of communication systems will continue. Technological advances and economics of scale are bound to lower costs so much that they will no longer be a hindrance to communication, international or national, whether the communication involves the human voice, text, pictures, or computer data.

An International System — Cross-Purposes Threaten Unity

Once an area of international cooperation, communication is becoming instead a source of international problems.

For many years cooperation dominated. This was partly due to the international nature of science and technology. Cooperation was partly achieved through the International Telecommunications Union, which provided technical standards that, in turn, enabled systems of different countries to work together in international communication. To some degree, the ITU works out international allocations of radio frequencies among various governments; it also fosters scientific and technological research necessary for the advance of communication, or for the adaptation of the relevant technology to new lands and new circumstances. It does not, of itself, provide communication, nor does it seek to establish a mechanism through which all negotiations concerning international communication must be channeled. Because of its cooperative and international character, the ITU functioned admirably for many years.

With the advent of communications satellites, a new concept of international cooperation was introduced. Fostered by the Communications Satellite Act and the establishment of the Communications Satellite Corporation, this concept flowered in the negotiations that led to the creation of an international consortium, Intelsat. What was new here was not the concept of communication across national boundaries, which was old and established, but of communication through an international communication system. The aim was high, the difficulties great, the entire concept revolutionary rather than evolutionary. It meant that in some way the needs and aspirations of *all* nations had to be considered before any pair or group of nations could apply available technology to the satisfaction of their own pressing communication needs.

This new international look has led to the upsetting of old patterns of action, to the injection of politics into the field of communication, and to endless agonizing delays in adapting new technology to pressing needs, national and international. The Soviet Union did not enter Intelsat, choosing instead to tackle its domestic communication problems by means of satellites before entering the international field. Among the major technological powers, only the Soviet Union has been spared the pain that came with the concept of an international satellite communication system.

The basic difficulty in international communication is that the needs of various nations differ profoundly. Some nations have no effective national system with which an international system can interact. Their prime need is to be able to communicate internally; external communication could then swiftly follow. Other nations have a great deal of international traffic, especially to certain points of commercial or political importance. For them, the application of the latest in modern communication technology is an urgent matter.

All nations must be able to choose freely among different communication technologies. In the international future, this means the choice between submarine cables and satellites. Such a choice may be made on several bases. In satellite communication, there is a time lapse of about a third of a second between transmission and reception. This can be serious in some circumstances. At present, the delay appreciably degrades voice transmission (though not to the point of rendering satellite circuits unusable). Economics is another important factor. For short distances cables are now cheaper, but for greater distances satellites are cheaper. Reliability is another consideration. Cables provide an alternative to satellite circuits. Privacy is still another consideration. Furthermore, two nations can lay a cable for their mutual communication without involving in any way the international allocation of the frequency spectrum or relations with other nations. For all these reasons, the improvement and extension of submarine cables are going ahead despite the rapid progress made in satellite technology.

As satellite communication develops, various nations and regions are becoming restive. The Canadians are planning their own system for communicating with their northern reaches. Germany and France are planning a European system adapted to their own particular needs. The Soviet Union is going its own way.

Thus the original American concept of an international satellite communication system faces many difficulties, only some of which are technical. The general experience in communication is that, granted a reasonable amount of technical standardization, it is easier, quicker, and better to solve problems locally and face up to the global problems later than it is to design a global system from scratch. Yet today we seem in principle to be faced with solving *all* the world's problems before we can solve any.

National sovereignty and regional needs are still an important part of international life. Perhaps in communication, as in other matters, we can make more rapid progress if we try to solve the pressing and tractable problems first, deferring a completely international solution until a day of higher technology and higher diplomatic achievement.

Communication in 2018

Technology, then, will provide us with increasingly cheap communication that knows no limitations of distance, and will serve man with increasing efficiency and flexibility. The transmission of pictures and texts and the distant manipulation of computers and other machines will be added to the transmission of the human voice on a scale that will eventually approach the universality of telephony. This will make electrical communication more like meeting people face to face. The tie-in with computers will put great information resources at the immediate disposal of those who are engaged in communication. But it seems unlikely that the language barrier will be overcome at an early date. This will have to await the day when computers can be made to understand areas of human knowledge and activity in a very real way. Although this is certainly possible, it may be a little slow in coming.

There is greater hope that television, national and international, will do something toward overcoming the language barrier. It can be helpful in achieving a commonality of language, or at least of a second language, within large nations such as India. It can be helpful in preventing English from degenerating into a variety of incomprehensible dialects, as it seems to be doing now. It is possible that mass communication as well as personal communication will extend the fraction of the world in which men possess in common a working knowledge of a language not their own in some field of their interest — scientific, technological, or business.

Communication, together with transportation, may eventually homogenize our world. Fortunately, there are forces working against this. Despite the best efforts of well-intentioned men, a certain variety of interest, aspiration, and even achievement will be preserved. It is through such differences that we can judge the potentialities of men on the one hand, and the results of various philosophies and courses of action on the other.

59

SUPPLEMENTARY MATERIAL

A. D. Hall, "Experiments with PICTUREPHONE Service," *Bell Laboratories Record,* April, 1964.

W. C. Hittinger and Morgan Sparks, "Microelectronics," *Scientific American,* November, 1965.

A. R. Michaelis, *From Semaphore to Satellite,* International Telecommunications Union, 1965.

J R. Pierce, *Waves and Messages,* Anchor Books, Doubleday and Company, Inc., Garden City, N.Y., 1967.

CHAPTER 5

WEATHER

Man Will Control Rain, Fog, Storms, and Even Possibly the Climate

by Thomas F. Malone

In retrospect, it is clear that our approach to the problems posed by nuclear energy and space travel, which have so dominated our thoughts in recent years, has been lamentably one-sided. Although we poured truly stupendous resources of time, brains, and money into developing the technologies of these two fields, somehow we never got around to giving much consideration to the international implications of what we were doing. Had we done so, mankind might have managed certain crises of the past few decades with more wisdom and foresight; and, correspondingly, the world outlook for the next five decades might not be so somber.

Let us not make the same mistake in the field of weather and climate control. I believe the next fifty years will be crucial in the development of the technologies necessary for controlling, to a significant extent, this particularly sensitive part of our physical environment. But the coming half-century will also be crucial in a much broader sense. It will be a testing period for our society — a chance for us to fashion, in advance, a milieu in which technical advancement can take place in the service, not of narrow national aggrandizement, but of all mankind.

To achieve this in regard to weather control, several steps will be required. We must deepen our understanding of the scientific problem —

Thomas F. Malone is chairman of the Committee on Atmospheric Sciences of the National Academy of Sciences, and Vice-President and Director of Research of The Travelers Insurance Company.

the opportunities it brings within reach, the limitations it imposes. We must perfect technological dexterity where it has been developed and develop it where it does not now exist. We must assess social and economic benefits and penalties, and weigh trade-offs. We must ascertain the biological consequences of deliberate intervention in the physical environment involved in ecosystems. We must resolve legal and jurisdictional complications. Above all, we must set about the difficult task of creating or adapting the international institutions that will be required if the potental hazards to international relations are to be avoided and the opportunities are to be seized.

The Need for Cooperation Is Clear

The warning flags have already been hoisted. The modest hopes and the quiet concern of the scientific community are a matter of record. The subject has been explored in both the executive and the legislative branches of the United States government. More than a decade ago, John Von Neumann[1] called attention to weather or climate modification as the kind of technological development that must be mastered through "a long sequence of small, correct decisions" if our society is, in his words, to survive technology. Pointing out that "measures in the arctic may control the weather in temperate regions, or measures in one temperate region critically affect another one, one-quarter around the globe," Von Neumann concluded: "All this will merge each nation's affairs with those of every other, more thoroughly than the threat of a nuclear or any other war may already have done."

Similar views have been expressed by meteorologists.[2] In an invited lecture on weather modification before the Fifth Congress of the World Meteorological Organization in 1967, Academician E. K. Federov,[3] chief of the Soviet Hydrometeorological Service, remarked:

> It is not difficult to understand that the problem of transforming the climate on a world or regional scale is, by its very nature, an international one, requiring the united efforts and the coordination of the activities of all countries. Ever more rapidly humanity is approaching the stage, in its symbiosis with nature, when it can turn to practical account all the natural resources of the earth and when, as a result, it will become capable of thinking in terms of natural phenomena on a planetary scale. . . .

It is hardly necessary to prove that, in these circumstances, all mankind should regard itself as a single whole in relation to the surrounding world. There is no other way.

A panel of the National Academy of Sciences[4] stated the case succinctly in 1966:

It is clear that a long-range program of weather control and climate modification can have a direct bearing upon relations between nations. It can aid the economic and social advancement of the less-developed countries, many of which face problems associated with hostile climates and serious imbalances in soil and water resources. And, quite importantly, it can serve to develop common interests among all nations and thus be a stimulus for new patterns of international cooperation.

In addition, a special commission of the National Science Foundation[5] presented the opportunity in these terms:

Rarely has a more inviting opportunity been offered for advanced thinking and planning regarding the impact of a technological development upon international relations.

In a report on weather modification and control prepared by the Legislative Reference Service of the Library of Congress[6] at the request of Warren E. Magnuson, chairman of the Senate Committee on Commerce, there appears this statement:

Whether the increased applications of weather modification become a factor in promoting international peace or in contributing to world tensions may be determined in part by the pattern of international cooperation and regulation that is established *during the current early stages of the subject.* [The italics are mine.]

These statements would appear to provide sufficient motivation for an examination of the scientific problem and some of its implications.

Wide-Scale Weather Control as a Scientific Problem

We may think of the atmosphere as a complex physical system in which the movement of air, changes in temperature, and the transformation of water into one or another of its phases — liquid, solid, and gaseous — are all of considerable practical interest, and are all taking place in response to certain forces or through particular processes. Although the atmosphere is far from being a tidy little deterministic system, in principle we can — by altering the forces or interfering with the processes — influence the motion of air, changes in temperature, and the phase transformations of water. In this sense, the matter of weather modification is a meaningful scientific problem.

It is, however, a complicated one. The earth's atmosphere may be viewed as an envelope rotating relative to the earth as well as with it. The relative motion arises from the forces associated with both the rotation of the earth and with sources and sinks of energy that vary in number, location, and strength. These sources and sinks depend on the distribution of shortwave solar radiation, the flux of outgoing longwave radiation, the latent heat involved in the change in phase of water, the transfer of sensible heat between the atmosphere and the underlying surface, and finally on the air motion itself. The kinetic energy of air motion exists in an array of scale sizes that extend from planetary wave systems down to molecular movement. There is a continuous exchange of kinetic energy from one scale to another, and kinetic energy is continually being exchanged with other forms of energy in the atmosphere.

The quantities of energy involved in weather systems and processes occurring naturally in the atmosphere substantially exceed the quantities under the control of man. For example, a thunderstorm may dissipate energy at the rate of 10^{11} calories per second, a hurricane at the rate of 10^{12}, and an extratropical cyclone at the rate of 10^{14}. By comparison, the rate of production of electrical energy over all the world was 10^{11} calories per second in 1962. On the other hand, the incremental energy released to the atmosphere by increasing rainfall by one-tenth of an inch over a hundred square miles (not an unrealistic objective) is equivalent to the total output of electrical energy in the United States in a six-day period. Thus, even though it is clear that the scientific problem of weather modification is solvable in principle, the outlook would be pessimistic for the foreseeable future were it not for two characteristics of the atmosphere: an intrinsic tendency toward certain instabilities, and the key role of the processes at the interface between the atmosphere and the underlying surface in determining the energy inputs into the atmosphere.

The attribute of instability is readily apparent, from everyday experience, in the tendency of the amplitude of atmospheric disturbances to increase with time. For example, a small, puffy-type cloud may grow to a towering thunderstorm in a matter of hours; a gentle zephyr in tropical latitudes may develop into a "killer" hurricane in a matter of days; and a small, low-pressure center may grow to a vigorous extratropical cyclone within a single day.

We are just beginning to understand the instability of supercooled water droplets, which, when released, provide a local source of sensible energy; the convective instability of a rising current of air within which water vapor is condensing into liquid, thus affecting the vertical distribution of sensible energy; and the so-called baroclinic instability of the large-scale, planetary atmospheric waves, which, when released, can profoundly alter the nature of the great global system of winds. Should it turn out that the upward progression of energy through this spectrum of instabilities is a process of considerable significance, an avenue may be opened whereby relatively modest but highly selective human interventions can produce large effects. We could, then, break the egg rather than slay the dragon.

Similarly, the sensitivity of the atmosphere to the interplay of the variables that determine the flux of energy between the atmosphere and the underlying land or water is beginning to yield to numerical analyses and field measurement. The consequences of altering surface parameters such as roughness, reflecting power, and the transfer of water across the interface is becoming known, and the possibility that these effects range beyond a local area are being explored.

How Climate Can Change Radically

Some support for the line of reasoning that links small causes with large effects is found in the results of an examination of massive fluctuations in climate that have occurred in the past. Although no adequate theory of climatic change exists today, there is reason to believe that these fluctuations — some of which would be disastrous to modern civilization — may have been caused by the triggering of instabilities by natural processes, through which a given climatic regime was transformed into a radically different one.

For any thoughtful consideration of climatic change, it is useful to have in mind a time scale for purposes of reference. We now know that "Spaceship Earth" was launched, in a manner we do not yet fully understand, a little more than five billion years ago. Geological evidence suggests that the first elementary forms of life appeared about three billion years ago. The date for the first indications of prehistoric man has been receding almost yearly as new discoveries find their way into scientific literature, but three million years ago appears to be the right order of magnitude. Modern man — with approximately the physical and intellectual potential of 20th-century man — emerged about fifty thousand years ago.

The sequence of early ice ages (each of roughly fifty million years' duration) that began in the late pre-Cambrian (from 700 to 800 million years ago), returned during the early Cambrian (500 million years ago), and returned once more in the Permian (230 million years ago), subjected early plant and animal life to a set of alternating stresses and relaxations that profoundly influenced evolutionary change. The salient characteristics of the ice ages included glaciers that covered 30 percent of continental areas and extended down to middle latitudes, much storminess, excessively cool and wet conditions just below the middle latitudes, and a narrow belt of hot and dry conditions on either side of a warm, wet equator. During the periods between the ice ages, the permanent ice sheet disappeared and relatively storm-free, dry, and mild conditions prevailed throughout middle latitudes.

Not only man's forebears, but also man himself have had to survive the invasion into middle latitudes of ice sheets thousands of feet thick. The most recent ice age began a million years ago, reaching a peak with the Günz Glacial that started 600,000 years ago. Since then we have had three glacial periods, the most recent being the Würm Glacial, which appeared 115,000 years ago and ended somewhere between 10,000 and 25,000 years ago with the advent of the Recent Interglacial Period in which we are now living.

Climatic fluctuations similar in character but somewhat smaller in amplitude have occurred in the last 8,000 years. Mildness from 4000 to 2000 B.C. and again from A.D. 400 to 1000 was interspersed with more stormy, glacial-type conditions from 1000 B.C. to A.D. 300 and again during the 13th and 14th centuries. The characteristics of forests and vegetation, the location and migration of people, the rise and fall of civilizations in the Mediterranean and Central America, and the routes by which America was "discovered" were all influenced by climatic conditions.

The Dust-Bowl Era of the 1930's made famous by the westward migration of the "Okies," the great northeastern drought of the early 1960's that compelled restrictions on water usage in New York City, and the near starvation of millions in India in the mid-1960's serve to remind us of man's dependence on even short-period aberrations in weather and climate.

New Horizons in Research

The problem of weather modification is passing from an era notable for intellectually undisciplined speculation and more-or-less opportunistic field experimentation into an era in which rational and organized inquiry can be conducted by exploring a set of meaningful scientific questions with a combination of computerized analytical techniques and carefully designed field experimentation. This transformation has its origin in four scientific and technological developments:

1. Understanding of the physical processes occurring in the atmosphere has now progressed to the point at which they can be expressed in equations that constitute mathematical models. These models permit the simulation of natural processes or — of particular relevance to our topic — the assessment of the consequences of human intervention in them. Although crude and oversimplified relative to the processes they are intended to simulate, useful models have been constructed of atmospheric phenomena that range in size from a single cloud to circulation of air over an entire hemisphere. There is almost unlimited potential for extension and refinement.

2. Development of the modern high-speed computer (which was encouraged initially by the computational needs of the nonlinear partial differential equations constituting the meteorological models) has proceeded simultaneously with the growth in sophistication of these atmospheric models. New generations of computers promise to bring within the realm of reality experiments by simulation that have hitherto been only a gleam in the eye of the meteorologist. Some of the more difficult problems of nonlinear instability will soon be within reach as both the speed and the capacity of computers continue to increase.

3. Our capabilities are expanding to make meaningful observations and measurements that specify the initial and final atmospheric conditions that must be reconciled by the computerized atmospheric models. The emerging capabilities range from the use of meteorologic satellites on a global scale to intricate measurements of the relevant physical characteristics of a single cloud.

4. Significant advances have been made in the power of modern statistical procedures for resolving questions of cause and effect relation-

ships in field experiments by establishing appropriate "design criteria" for both research and operational projects. The collaboration between individuals skilled in these procedures and experimental meteorologists is really only beginning, but it already promises important contributions to reducing ambiguity in the interpretation of weather-modification activities.

Taken together, these four advances provide the basis for believing that the exploration of weather modification has reached a take-off point from which further progress will take place at an accelerating rate. Quite clearly, within the next decade or so it will become possible to explore, through simulation techniques, an almost unlimited array of deliberate interventions in natural atmospheric processes, and to assess possibilities and limitations. These studies will inevitably lead to specific requirements for meteorological measurements and carefully designed field experiments that will deepen our understanding of natural processes and test the efficacy of intervention in them. Mathematical models of the atmosphere have already been used in a preliminary way to assess the consequences of the inadvertent intervention associated with the increase of atmospheric carbon dioxide. These models can be used to define the tolerable limits to this large-scale geophysical experiment that mankind is undertaking, or, alternatively, to determine desirable countervailing measures.

How Man Will Control the Weather

At the risk of oversimplification and with the usual caveats about fallibility, the present position and some judgmental evaluations of the future prospects for weather modification can be summarized as follows:

1. Field results have demonstrated unequivocally that several cubic miles of supercooled clouds (liquid cloud droplets at temperatures below freezing) can be transformed into ice-crystal clouds by seeding with appropriate chemicals. The technology for performing this kind of weather modification will be perfected rapidly over the next decade.

2. Dissipation of supercooled fog over an airfield runway is now operationally feasible and has been used to good economic advantage by airlines in the United States and in other nations. Further improvement in technique will likely affect only the economics, not the efficacy, of this control measure.

3. Recent experimentation in clearing certain types of "warm" fog (droplets at temperatures above freezing) over airports is beginning to

produce encouraging results. An important breakthrough in this type of highly localized weather control is likely to be realized in a matter of years.

4. Relatively little serious attention has been given to conscious interference in the processes at the interface between the atmosphere and the underlying surface beyond demonstrating that it is possible to inhibit evaporation from water surfaces and vegetation. If, as it now appears to be likely, these interface processes turn out to be important to large-scale modification of the climate, there is a high probability that the technology could go through explosive development in the period from 1975 to 1995.

5. Persuasive, although by no means conclusive, evidence suggests that rainfall can be increased through cloud seeding by from 5 to 20 percent (say 10 percent), depending on the conditions. There is a high probability that residual ambiguity will be resolved by 1975, and a further high probability that by 1980 naturally occurring rainfall can be either augmented or diminished locally by proved techniques. The probability is high that by 1990 rainfall several hundred miles downwind from the site of the operations can be increased or decreased at will.

6. There are indications that Soviet scientists have succeeded in reducing hail damage by a factor of from three to five by introducing silver iodide directly into susceptible parts of hail-producing clouds. This form of weather modification will probably always remain local, but will develop rapidly over the next decade, and there is a high probability that it will begin to be adopted for widespread use by the early 1980's.

7. Physically reasonable approaches to the suppression of lightning have been tried with what appears, on balance, to be promising results. Progress on this highly localized modification measure will be retarded pending a satisfactory explanation for the lightning discharge process, but the probabilities are high that operational techniques will be available by the late 1980's.

8. Cloud-seeding techniques that are of sufficient merit to warrant field experimentation have been advanced for the modification of hurricanes. The limited tests have not as yet yielded even preliminary conclusions. This approach should be pursued vigorously, but the probability of success is not high — only about 50 percent. New concepts are needed, and they are likely to emerge from computer simulation of hurricanes. If five years are allowed for the development of an adequate mathematical model, five more years for assessing the consequences of interventions of

various kinds, and then ten years of field experimentation for validation, it seems unreasonable to expect much before 1990, with the probabilities fair to good that a proved technology will exist by the year 2000.

9. No technique for consciously influencing large-scale weather patterns yet exists and not much progress can be expected for another decade until the scientific results of the recently approved Global Atmospheric Research Program[7] begin to be available. The 1970's should be a productive and exciting decade for basic research on the general circulation of the atmosphere. The 1980's and 1990's should be an equally productive period of experimentation, by means of computer simulation, on the technology of large-scale climate modification. The probability of success in broad climate modification is likely to exceed 50 percent by the year 2018.

10. A distinct probability should be recognized that large-scale climate modification will be effected inadvertently before the power of conscious modification is achieved. Calculations with the relatively crude large-scale atmospheric models at hand suggest that the from 10 to 15 percent increase in the minute amount of carbon dioxide in the atmosphere since 1900 has caused surface temperatures to rise $0.2°C$, while temperatures in the stratosphere may have decreased ten times as much. It should be possible by 1980 to predict with precision the effects on the atmosphere in the year 2018 of the likely rate at which carboniferous fuel is being consumed. There is a small probability that these effects will not be tolerable. Air pollution may have already extended its influence beyond the urban domain. Contamination of the upper atmosphere by rocket exhaust is a problem that may be of practical importance sooner than we realize. Finally, agricultural cultivation and urbanization are transforming the nature of the surface underlying the atmosphere on a large-scale basis, with possibly important consequences that we should be able to assess during the 1980's.

Global Consequences Call for Global Controls

For purposes of assessing the international implication of weather modification, it is useful to divide modification activities into four classes:

1. Local intervention that produces only local results (for example, fog dissipation, lightning and hail suppression, and certain kinds of rain augmentation or diminution).

2. Local intervention that may produce significant changes tens or

hundreds of miles downstream (for example, certain kinds of rainfall modification, or tampering with hurricanes).

3. Intervention over a large area, or concerted operations at several points, aimed at restructuring climatic regimes (for example, interference with exchange processes at the interface between the atmosphere and the underlying surface).

4. Inadvertent intervention that has slow-response, long-term effects on the global climate (for example, alterations in atmospheric structure resulting from an increase in carbon dioxide as a consequence of combustion processes, or contamination of the upper atmosphere by rocket exhaust).

The first class of weather modification activity poses few, if any, international problems.

The second class presents issues involving conventional concepts of national sovereignty supported by existing international law. These include, for example, the right to maintain national territory (including air space) free of physical interference on the part of other nations; the right to control the acts of individuals on national territory; the right to protect the lives, property, and interests of nationals from the acts of others; and finally the right to indemnification when the action of one nation or its nationals infringes on another nation or its nationals.

There is no reason to believe that these issues require more than conventional international mechanisms for resolution. It is quite possible, however, that an appropriate mechanism would have to be established or an existing one adapted for the purpose. The availability of a responsive and effective international organization is essential for the peaceful solution of any conflict of national interests that might arise.

The third and the fourth classes of weather modification activity share in common the characteristic that each is concerned with the global environmental consequences of human activity. In one case, the global consequences follow directly from the human activity; in the other, they follow indirectly. With regard to deliberate intervention, one or more mechanisms or international agencies are needed to decide, on behalf of the world community, what can and should be done, to implement these decisions, and to regulate national activities in such a way as to minimize international conflict.

With regard to inadvertent intervention, a mechanism is needed to determine the global consequences of contemporary human activities and to see that these consequences do not cross the threshold of tolerability from the viewpoint of mankind as a whole. Possibly this international body could be given policing powers and perhaps the authority to implement countervailing measures when human activities affect the global environment deleteriously.

The foregoing functions are not intended to be complete. The conclusion is inescapable, however, that entirely new dimensions of international cooperation will have to be explored to meet the needs that may develop from progress in weather modification between now and the year 2018.

It is probably unrealistic — and might even be undesirable at this instant in history — to create immediately the international instruments necessary to fulfill all these conceivable functions. However, in the spirit of Von Neumann's admonition that "a long sequence of small, correct decisions" will be required, I venture to suggest a discrete step that seems to me to be warranted in view of the imminence of the year 2018. Any action that is contemplated should satisfy these criteria: (1) It should be a modest step and should avoid sensationalism; (2) it should seek to fill in the gaps in our knowledge and lay as solid a foundation of fact as is possible for any future decisions that may need to be made; and (3) it should be international, interdisciplinary, and as nonpolitical as possible.

These criteria would appear to be met by assembling, under the auspices of the International Council of Scientific Unions (ICSU), a small, permanent, full-time working group charged with the responsibility of exploring in depth the scientific and other aspects of the problem, and reporting its findings and recommendations back to the world community through ICSU from time to time. The highest standard of intellectual excellence should be established for participation, and membership on the working group should be drawn from nominations by the national organizations represented in ICSU. Membership should include physical scientists with experience in the atmospheric sciences, oceanography, natural-resource analysis, physics, mathematics, and chemistry. It should also involve life scientists with a special interest in ecosystems, social scientists with a special interest in economics and international relations, and legal scholars with a particular interest in international law. The hard core of a dozen or so senior members should be supported by a number of research associates and provided with the advanced computational facilities for sophisticated simulation studies.

Adequate and stable support should be assured for at least ten years by voluntary national contributions or through an agency, such as UNESCO, that sponsors general international scientific work. Appropriate liaison should be maintained with the Joint Organizing Committee that ICSU has established, in cooperation with the World Meteorological Organization, to provide guidance to the Global Atmospheric Research Program, which is concerned with the scientific problems of the general circulation of the global atmosphere and with the development of physical methods for long-range forecasting.

It should be clearly recognized that the objectives of the proposed ICSU working group, with its emphasis on determining the technological feasibility of weather and climate modification and some of the implications involved, differ in several major respects from the activities of the Joint Organizing Committee. The highly successful efforts of the ICSU Committee on Atmospheric Sciences, which, under the aegis of the International Union of Geodesy and Geophysics (IUGG), led to international unanimity on the Global Atmospheric Research Program, suggest that a proved pattern of international cooperation has been laid. Activities such as the International Geophysical Year, the International Year of the Quiet Sun, and the International Biological Program, support the point of view that international non-governmental organizations such as ICSU and IUGG can play important roles in this undertaking.

I do not presume to believe that the step I have suggested, if taken, is sufficient by itself, but it is a positive action with important consequences that cannot be foreseen in detail at this time.

U.S. Goals Encompass Cooperation on Weather

Even a cursory examination of international cooperative projects leads to the conclusion that in the present-day world the survival and effectiveness of any particular activity are in direct proportion to the degree that the activity supports national interests. It is desirable, therefore, to test the program I have here proposed in the light of this fact.

In the international field, the U.S. national objective and the basic elements of our foreign policy in support of this objective were spelled out a few years ago with remarkable clarity by Secretary of State Dean Rusk.[8] The national objective, he declared, is "a peaceful world of independent nations, each free to choose its own institutions so long as it does not threaten the freedom of others and all free to cooperate in their common interests and in the welfare of mankind." The basic elements of foreign policy, then, are fivefold: (1) To build the strength of the free world and to protect it against aggression; (2) to enlarge and improve our partnership with the other economically advanced nations of the free world; (3) to assist the less developed nations in advancing economically, socially, and politically; (4) to improve and strengthen the organizations and institutions that enable the nations of the world to work together more effectively; and (5) to seek, earnestly and untiringly, areas of common interest with our adversaries.

Not a great deal of imagination is required to envision the manner in which each of these elements could be supported by a carefully considered program to prepare for what may turn out to be, over the next fifty years, one of the major confrontations between public policy and new technological capabilities. If this support moves us one step forward to the national objective stated above, the interests of all mankind will have been well served.

NOTES

1. John Von Neumann, "Can We Survive Technology," *Fortune*, Vol. 51, June, 1955, p. 106 *et seq.*
2. Thomas F. Malone, "Some Implications of Progress in the Atmospheric Sciences," *Monographie No. 16* of the International Union of Geodesy and Geophysics, January, 1962.
3. E. K. Federov, "Weather Modifications," *WMO Bulletin,* Vol. XVI, No. 3, July, 1967, pp. 122-130.
4. National Academy of Sciences-National Research Council, "Final Report of the Panel on Weather and Climate Modification to the Committee on Atmospheric Sciences, Weather and Climate Modification Problems and Prospects," NAS Publication No. 1350, Washington, D.C., 1966.
5. National Science Foundation, "Weather and Climate Modification," NSF Report 66-3 of the Special Commission on Weather Modification, Washington, D.C., 1966.
6. Legislative Reference Service, Library of Congress (L. M. Hartman, with the assistance of R. L. Thornton and Mrs. E. C. Collier), "Weather Modification and Control," Report No. 1139, Eighty-Ninth Congress, Second Session, U.S. Government Printing Office, Washington, D.C., 1966.
7. Committee on Atmospheric Sciences, "Report of the Study Conference on the Global Atmospheric Research Program (GARP)," International Council of Scientific Unions, Stockholm, July, 1967.
8. Dean Rusk, "Foreign Policy and the American Citizen," an address made before the Farmer's Union Grain Terminal Association, St. Paul, Minn., Dec. 10, 1963 (available from the Office of Media Services, Bureau of Public Affairs, State Department, Washington, D.C., Series S-No. 16).

CHAPTER 6

EDUCATIONAL TECHNOLOGY

Electronics May Revolutionize Education, But Is Unlikely to Solve Problems of Human Frailty

by Anthony G. Oettinger

Like so many things nowadays, education is said to be exploding. Once education, like cod-liver oil, was something to be administered only to boys too big for swaddling but too small for swords. Now, as the founders of the Nova Schools in Fort Lauderdale, Fla., like to put it, education covers all the years from prenatal to post-probate. We do not yet treat this widening span as a continuum, so I must distinguish between formal conventional education, administered to minors and young adults by institutions ranging from kindergarten to college, and adult education, administered haphazardly and in a variety of ways to the layman and to the diplomat. I will look at both in turn.

In the long run, educational technology is bound to affect international diplomacy in proportion to its success in inducing or supporting significant changes in the type or the level of formal education in either our own or other nations. It seems fair to maintain that, on the whole,

Anthony G. Oettinger is a professor of applied mathematics at Harvard University, and president of the Association for Computing Machinery.

educational technology is somewhat more advanced in the United States than in other nations. Hence, the external effect depends also on the extent to which both our successes and our failures with technological innovations are imitated elsewhere in the world. Both sides of the innovation coin must be mentioned. Many things have speeded up, but years of lead time are still required nowadays to nurture a laboratory seedling into a forest of sturdy applications. Incipient failures may therefore be transplanted as often as incipient successes, and the more delicate plants may wither in indifferent soils.

The Instant University Is Possible

Many rosy pictures have been painted of the future of educational technology. I yield to no man in my ambitions as a seer. In an earlier paper[1] I noted that modern technology can make it possible for sound, pictures, and even objects stored at appropriate centers to be made available with the greatest of ease and, with a bit of wishful thinking, at negligible cost at innumerable local points of access. These points might be schools, libraries, factories, or, with just a bit more stretching of the imagination, homes.

Thus, one can visualize a world in which anyone anywhere might have ready access to great libraries and their books, to videotape or film libraries containing lessons on specialized topics, to records of significant contemporary or past events, to outstanding dramatic productions, to a difficult operation particularly well performed in a leading hospital, and to a particularly smooth negotiation by particularly wise diplomats. The same system would also supply teaching programs of the kind already in widespread experimental use and a variety of tools to aid in symbol manipulation and concept formation, including dictionaries, thesauri, currency-conversion tables, war games, peace games, and the like.

The teaching programs would give routine directions through the maze of available materials. Many of the documents in the consulting collections might themselves contain references to other entries. The whole library system could thus be visualized as a kind of gargantuan version of Vannevar Bush's Memex.[2]

There is much food for thought in the question of whether underdeveloped countries need recapitulate the rocky Western road to literacy and universal education. The widespread use of transistor radios, television, holography, and other media linked by satellite communication could lead to cultural developments based on a combination of oral and pictorial communication modes that may, but need not, include the conventional printed word.

One can speculate that even in the Western world the existing germs of computer-aided symbolic and pictorial manipulation will lead to a profound revolution in our patterns of thought and communication and, therefore, of education. By using computers to manipulate pictorial information in two or more dimensions, we gain an important quality lacking in the printed page, namely the variability of an image with time. Not only can we present a sequence of images, as in books or movies, but a single image as well can be grown, viewed from varying standpoints, superimposed on or merged with another, or changed in form right before one's eyes at the command of either man or machine.

Predicting precisely what effects these new abilities will have is as difficult as inferring the possibility of a Shakespeare or a Newton before the invention of writing. I do believe, however, that these effects will be as striking.

TV Will Saturate the World With Electronic Culture

But, as I have written elsewhere, there is a gap between such visions and reality.[3] Immature technology and overripe institutions unite to make it most likely that ten years from now formal education here and abroad will go on pretty much as it does now. Innovation, whether dependent on technology, spurred by technology, or sparked by any other creative impulse, is slow to make its mark felt on educational systems. The few shining examples of progress will be hothouse plants that wither or lose their fragrance in any but their native pot. Excessive political emphasis on immediate results will divert resources from research and development, and thereby delay the realization of the visions.

I can more easily convince myself that the widening of international voice and television communications will be a significant factor over the forthcoming decade. For one thing, I know less about technological problems in that field. Minds are bound to be penetrated when satellites enable a rapid worldwide exchange of television programs. Sooner or later, even the most underdeveloped of nations can be saturated by the electronic culture described by Marshall McLuhan. This is education of sorts. It will have profound effects on a world where the ears of youth on both sides of the Iron Curtain already belong to jazz and rock 'n' roll.

The more formal uses of classroom television have been none too success-ful in this country to date.[4] Whether, like ancient taxicabs, these mistakes will be exported to South America is something I am not competent to predict.

Push-Button Diplomacy, Too

By far the most critical impact of educational technology on inter-national diplomacy could be felt in the realm of adult education. It seems neither inaccurate nor unfair to characterize diplomacy as a form of mutual adult education. Adult education is also the aim of the elaborate processes by which our State Department and other agencies and their counterparts abroad provide information to government policy- and decision-makers.

It is as easy in this realm, as in that of formal education, to conjure up visions of technological revolutions. Two examples will do. It is easy enough, for example, to leap from a demonstration of Picturephone transmission between New York and Washington to an image of instant diplomacy conducted by means of pictorial "hot lines" among the capi-tals of the world. World leaders can be literally face-to-face like mer-chants in a bazaar. One can also extrapolate from current experiments with computer-based information-retrieval systems and their applications in relatively limited situations to a vision of a vast computerized informa-tion network. The network would store all information relevant to diplo-macy and international decision-making and make the information available to decision-makers at the push of a button.

Belief in a transcendent efficacy of modern technology and fear of a concomitant satanic power are nowadays widespread and deeply held convictions. The depth of such convictions among laymen is matched only by their ignorance of technology and technologists. Unfortunately, therefore, when reverence has the upper hand, responsibility is unwisely delegated to technicians. When fear predominates, heads plunge into the sand. Little ground is inhabited between "Let's buy a gross of each" and "Trust human affairs to robots? — Never!"

In a talk to State Department officials reported in the department's *Newsletter,*[5] John Diebold urged them to specify what they wanted from technology for, as he put it, "If we know, we can get it." This sort of cheery confidence is misplaced for any but the most limited and carefully spelled-out objectives.

I am not arguing that goals should never be spelled out, although often this is asking too much. However, to state that merely saying where we want to go is enough to get us there and, by implication, get us there through technological means alone is gross oversimplification at best. Two distinctions are worth remembering in this context. The first is between sensible goals for research and development and sensible prospects for immediate application and exploitation. This distinction is a fine one, all too rarely observed in a climate where long-term research and development must be justified to the public and to Congress in terms of immediate applications and rewards. The second distinction is between using a tool well and whacking your thumb with it.

Technology's Bittersweet Harvest

Technology serves human aims in human organizations manned by human beings moved by emotions and engaged in office politics as well as in diplomacy or education. The rabid technician's dream of an aseptic world run by tireless, efficient robots is as absurd as rabid neo-Luddite assaults on punched cards. Applying technology, like all human efforts, bears bittersweet fruits.

Excepting such indirect and uninformative manifestations as punched-card bills, computer-printed bank statements, and *New Yorker* cartoons, computers, like other recent products of science and technology, are still remote from common lay experience. I feel I cannot, in this brief space, convey enough intuitive feeling for their promises and their limitations. Consider, instead, an anecdote drawn from more common and intelligible experience. Think of computers where I speak of a car or a plane. The individual and collective human environment in which these vehicles function is qualitatively comparable to that of computers. I think the delicate balance between progress and chaos, between technological amplification of human powers and technological failure, between human resourcefulness and human frailty, is characteristic as well of computer applications.

I recently flew from Boston to New York in less than an hour. By evening, the chaos induced by a combination of bad weather and equipment failure had made all airline schedules so erratic that instead I rented a car to return home. Well along on the Connecticut Turnpike, as my windshield suddenly grew opaque from slush spattered on it, I discovered that the windshield washer on my car was not functioning. I limped to the nearest toll gate, where a collector directed me to the next exit where I might find a gas station. I drove off the highway and not only found the gas station closed, but also no entrance to match the exit. A half-hour hunt in unfamiliar territory finally produced a gas station. The attendant diagnosed my trouble as a missing cap on an open branch in the path to the windshield squirter, from which the diverted water spurted on the engine. With quick mechanical ingenuity he picked a nail off the floor of his shop and rammed it into the opening to plug it. He then directed me back to the turnpike. I was home a little more than four hours after leaving the airport. Before the advent of turnpikes the same trip under the best of conditions took about eight hours.

The story is a parable of the mixture of human intelligence and folly, of technological accomplishment and failure, that characterizes all technology — including computers. Yet the layman's relationship with computers has grown to be a love-and-hate affair with overtones of idolatry. Hatred is implicit in Seligman's description of what he calls "the technicist ethos" as "a combination of practices and attitudes which suggest that the world and its inhabitants are little more than a mechanical contrivance." [6] Reverence is suggested by his arrant misconception that "digital calculations lead to inexorable, inescapable conclusions." Pontification is a human, not a mechanical, vice. A much more frequent role for the computer and, indeed, for much of technology is either that of the Trojan Horse bringing institutional reform inside otherwise impregnable gates, or that of the scapegoat for otherwise inexplicable failures of policy or action.

Human Frailty Stymies Progress

Just having technology around is not enough to assure its use, let alone its effective use. I delight in speculating on the effect worldwide Picturephone transmission or instant information-retrieval systems would have on our State Department. An interesting blend of technical problems, massive incompetence, or unkind Congressional supervision has, by its own account, left the State Department paralyzed before the telephone. The following comments, made in 1965 by State Department officials to Representative John J. Rooney of New York, explain the situation[7]:

> *Mr. Coffey:* In most instances, sir, we are dependent upon regular commercial telephone, and in most instances the tele-

phone is not used as a day-to-day communication means.

Mr. Crockett: Because it is not secure enough.

It is not that the telephone is felt to be unnecessary:

Mr. Crockett: The problems today seemingly have gotten so acute you have to have a telephone to talk rather than wait on telegraph. . . .

In fact, secure systems are available, but they seem to have some failings:

Mr. Crockett: The telephone in Paris is often out of use because the techniques have improved and the techniques of the old system are not good enough.

This explanation may seem ambiguous if not foolish, but fortunately Mr. Coffey clarifies it:

The voice quality is not particularly good on long-distance circuits and the instruments are comparatively awkward to use because they have what is called a "push to talk" means. You do not have the capability of talking and listening at the same time.

This plaintive testimony in an era when telephones veritably grow out of the ears of American teen-agers epitomizes the plight inherent in the confrontation between modern technology, our diplomatic establishment, and Congress. Political limitations and the limited absorption rates of ancient institutions thus forestall the effective use of even existing technology.

Computers scarcely fare better in that setting. Witness the following exchange between Representatives Jack Brooks of Texas and Ogden R. Reid of New York[8]:

Mr. Brooks: If you will pardon me at this point, Mr. Reid, I believe the Department of State has not been aware of the advantages of ADP [Automatic Data Processing] as most agencies.

Mr. Reid: That is a Texas euphemism for a certain lack of vigor, I take it.

Needed: The Well-Trained Retriever

But what do computers have to do with the State Department? Like any other organization, the State Department has needs both modest and momentous. It has, for example, a payroll and personnel data. It surely is conscious also of the objective expressed by Congressman Reid as "the retrieval of answers to essential national questions."[9] It may even be conscious of the potential of technology to solve some of these problems. But, as T. S. Eliot put it:

> Between the desire
> And the spasm
> Between the potency
> And the existence
> Between the essence
> And the descent
> Falls the Shadow

Can computers satisfy the State Department's weak desire? The search for answers must span the range from the pettiest details of bureaucratic organization to the information explosion.

International diplomacy, like almost every other form of human endeavor, is afflicted nowadays by explosions. Computers are commonly prescribed to the executives of business organizations suffering from information explosion. The effectiveness of computer therapy is a tricky question I have discussed elsewhere,[10] but this entire range of problems assumes a special poignancy in the case of the State Department, as Smith Simpson has indicated:

> Even the introduction of computers to dispel that "ghost that haunts the policy officer" has lagged, partly from lack of funds, partly from incompetence. A department that must use obsolescent typewriters and adding machines which cost more for repairs than they are worth is not likely to invest heavily in computers. And, at least for the time being, such an investment might be dubious in any case. The people responsible for operating the few computers the department has been able to wangle have been trying for some two years to master the intricacies of printing out simple personnel data. Any broad application of computers to foreign affairs, so as to permit the storage and instant retrieval of needed information, is clearly a long way off in the State Department.[11]

It seems implied by the foregoing quotation that only the State Department's ineptitude precludes the effective use of computer technology in foreign affairs. Indeed, citing the confusion following the Prime Minister of Singapore's statement some years ago that the C.I.A. had offered to bribe him, a statement followed first by State Department denials and later by his disclosure of a letter from Secretary of State Dean Rusk apologizing for the incident, Simpson says that the incident was unnecessary because "a computer would have spared the United States this and many another humiliation."

There are many reasons why this assumption — made in the tradition of "if you state the problem, we can solve it" — is much too optimistic.

Too Much Information, Please

Information explosion in the State Department, as in many other public and private institutions, has some roots in the tragicomedies of human affairs. Prescribing computers may encourage artificial dissemination where birth control might be more appropriate. Replying to Congressman Rooney's perennial question about the number of communications in the department, Idar Rimestad, Deputy Under Secretary for Administration, recently engaged in the following exchange[12]:

> *Mr. Rooney:* What is being done to cut down the number of communications?
>
> *Mr. Rimestad:* One of our problems is that we are inundated with paper. It represents constant pressure on the posts and on our people. We are asking them not to be so loquacious. I assure you in Paris we were after this practically every day. Communications would come across my desk or across the desk of another senior officer and we would see if we could cut down on the words that were going to Washington. This is a real problem.
>
> *Mr. Rooney:* You have described a situation which we have known about for a long time. What is really being done about it is the question.
>
> *Mr. Rimestad:* We are putting constant pressure on the ambassadors and embassies to cut down the flow of words and paper.
>
> *Mr. Rooney:* What success have you had?
>
> *Mr. Rimestad:* Unfortunately, I do not think we have been too successful but we are constantly seeking ways to improve the situation.

Putting broad-band communications, picture telephones, and instant computerized retrieval in the hands of such an organization is like feeding pastry to a fat man. The problem is clearly not only input but also digestion. Such problems are also widespread. As Crockett and Argyris both point out, "all systems, including universities, seem to be plagued with them." [13]

The input question is one that cannot be solved solely by technological legerdemain. Many people — diplomats and policy-makers are not immune — suffer from the delusion that any piece of data is valuable in itself, that more and better data mean more and better information, and that better information means better decisions.

The notion that one can or should acquire every bit of information relevant to a particular issue is surely a delusion. We have just seen that the State Department relies heavily on telegrams that, as written material, happen to lend themselves readily to reproduction and filing. The use of telegrams is, however, partly accidental. Some of their use is merely a consequence of faulty telephone service. One can easily imagine that, if the bulk of State Department communications traffic were telephonic, the department would think twice before asking, and Congressman Rooney would think twice before granting, funds for the apparatus necessary to record and for the staff necessary to transcribe every telephone conversation taking place in lieu of telegraphic substitutes already intrinsically cheaper.

But even barring such accidents, to assume that every piece of information bearing on a particular issue could be available to a policy-maker means assuming access to every library, every newspaper, every office, and every bedroom in the world.

Input at best is, therefore, a matter of sampling. Yet, to the best of my knowledge, the blind treatment of input data under the hypnotic persuasion that one is dealing with every available piece of information has precluded any serious study — let alone implementation — of the application of sampling techniques to the analysis and evaluation of diplomatic data. Consequently, much of what is received is never used, much of what is necessary is never received, and the how's and why's of input selection remain a mystery not yet subject to rational analysis. When President Johnson strives to restore the balance of payments by ordering a 10 percent cut in government personnel abroad, who can foretell the effect on the quality of sampling?

As for digestion, Vannevar Bush, who has often been misquoted by rabid information retrievers, said long ago that "the investigator is stag-

gered by the findings and conclusions of thousands of other workers —
many of which he cannot find time to grasp, much less to remember,
as they appear." [14] Karl Deutsch expressed the same thought when, in
another context, he pointed out that modern technology had mechanized
broadcasting or the loudspeaker, but had not mechanized listening.

Research on speech recognition has already led to some very simple
forms of mechanized listening, but none remotely adequate to the higher
forms of international diplomacy. Therefore, until we are able to replace
chiefs of state by robot equivalents, it is unlikely that technological innovation, however successful or however well applied, can be a panacea.
Deutsch makes this point rather well:

> It is perfectly possible right now for Mr. Brezhnev to telephone
> Mr. Johnson, but even if he should do so, it would still take him
> a while to figure out what the other fellow meant. Supposing
> you have telephone lines all over the world which will bring the
> leaders of the great powers of the world as close together as two
> Oriental rug merchants bargaining in a bazaar face to face, the
> haggling among them would not be noticeably speeded up, as
> it is not noticeably speeded up in the bazaars where there is no
> problem of getting the sound waves from one individual to
> the other.[15]

Questions About Questions Remain

Moreover, many perplexing policy questions bearing on the management of foreign diplomacy, just as on any other type of management,
are questions that cannot be resolved by technology, although technology
may shape the answers to some extent.

For example, it is a critical question whether the recipient of the ultimate output of an information system should be presented only with
carefully worked out recommendations based on consensus at all lower
levels of (mechanical or human) judgment and evaluation, or whether
he should have at his disposal an audit trail, so to speak, leading back
to raw data. Signposts along this trail might include statements of alternative points of view, the identity of their holders, and other signs disclosing
who (or what), under what circumstances, and with what degree of
presumptive reliability made what choice, what hypothesis, what implicit
decision. A computerized audit trail might, under some circumstances,
be easier or more economical to blaze than finding, collating, and prepar-

ing a bushel of footnotes, citations, or minority reports.

However, asking how the labeling of decisions, the provision of an audit trail, and similar practices would affect the decision-making process and alter the roles of all the players in this process is a question logically independent of the technological means for implementing the process. Such questions must continue to be asked and the search for answers must continue. No magic wand will wave them away. By opening wide the floodgates of information, technology has created, as it always does, both an opportunity and a threat. The remarkable machinery essential for making the most of it is where it has been for millennia — right above our noses.

NOTES

1. Anthony G. Oettinger, *A Vision of Technology and Education,* Reprint No. 1, Harvard Program on Technology and Society, Cambridge, Mass., 1966 (*Communications of the ACM,* Vol. 9, July, 1966, p. 487-490).
2. Vannevar Bush, "As We May Think," *Atlantic Monthly,* July, 1945, pp. 101-108.
3. Anthony G. Oettinger, *Run, Computer, Run: An Essay on Technology and Education,* Draft Report, Harvard Program on Technology and Society, Cambridge, Mass., 1968.
4. Carnegie Commission on Educational Television, *Public Television: A Program for Action,* Bantam Books, New York, 1967.
5. John Diebold, "Program Management and Computers and Foreign Affairs," *Foreign Affairs Quarterly,* Oct. 19, 1966.
6. B. B. Seligman, *Most Notorious Victory — Man in an Age of Automation,* The Free Press, New York, 1966, pp. 299-301.
7. Eighty-Eighth Congress, Second Session, *Hearings before a Subcommittee of the Committee on Appropriations,* House of Representatives, Government Printing Office, 1964 (Subcommittee on Department of State, Justice, etc., J. J. Rooney, Chairman) pp. 385-386.
8. Ninetieth Congress, First Session, *Data Processing Management in the Federal Government, Hearings before a Subcommittee of the Committee on Government Operations,* House of Representatives, July 18, 19 and 20, 1967, Government Printing Office, 1967, p. 103.
9. *Ibid.*
10. Anthony G. Oettinger, "A Bull's Eye View of Management and Engineering Information Systems," *Proceedings of the 19th National Conference (1964),* Association for Computing Machinery, New York, 1964.
11. S. Simpson, "Who Runs the State Department?" *The Nation,* March 6, 1967, p. 298.
12. Ninetieth Congress, First Session, *Hearings before a Subcommittee of the Committee on Appropriations,* House of Representatives, Government Printing Office, 1967 (Subcommittee on Department of State, Justice, etc., J. J. Rooney, Chairman) Part 2, p. 25.
13. C. Argyris, *Some Causes of Organizational Ineffectiveness within the Department of State,* Occasional Papers No. 2, Center for International Systems Research, Department of State, Washington, D.C. 1967 (Department of State Publication 8180, Superintendent of Documents, U.S. Government Printing Office).
14. Bush, *op. cit.*
15. Karl Deutsch, Columbia University Seminar on Technology and Social Change, 13 October 1966, Transcript pp. 6-7.

CHAPTER 7

BEHAVIORAL TECHNOLOGY

Man Will Win More Control Over His Destiny

by Ithiel de Sola Pool

The next half-century may well become the era of behavioral science. If this happens, it will be due not to any great new theory but rather to the application of many small technologies. It is a cliché that the social sciences are a hundred years behind the natural sciences. In this view, we are waiting for a Newton to burst forth with simple, basic, and powerful laws of human behavior, setting the social sciences off on the path of dramatic discovery that the natural sciences have followed for the past two hundred years. The notion is probably a misconception, the expectation an illusion.

In point of fact, the social sciences are as old as the natural sciences. Man has been the object of man's study for as long as he has studied nature. If the results are less than satisfactory, it is because the subject is inherently more difficult and less tractable than the physical sciences, not because we turned to the subject at a later date. And even without a Newton, we can nevertheless expect that the behavioral sciences, or more accurately behavioral technology, will play an ever larger role in the organization of society during the next fifty to one hundred years.

Ithiel de Sola Pool is professor of political science at Massachusetts Institute of Technology. Books he has written include Symbols of Democracy; American Business and Public Policy; The People Look at Educational Television; *and* Candidates, Issues, and Strategies.

The advances that will give man more control over his social destiny include discoveries in neurology, physiology, genetics, psychology, and mathematics, as well as in the physics and chemistry that underlie computer and communication technology. New insights may also come directly out of research in anthropology, sociology, and political science. And each of these discoveries and insights will add a little something to what we know about that vast, complex mass of interactions called society.

This newfound ability to understand and analyze, and thereby to control, extremely complex systems of many interacting variables will permit a quantum advance in behavioral technology in the next fifty years. For example, one such complex system, the prevention of war, will require, among other things:

— an understanding of unconscious human passions
— the ability to satisfy economic needs
— improved negotiating skills
— better communication among potential adversaries
— better organization of national and international governmental institutions
— changes in man's ideologies and values
— control of armaments technology.

Effective peace-keeping requires the ability to manipulate all these elements of a complex, multivariate system whose interactions can produce many unanticipated consequences. As our ability to analyze systems improves, we will make progress in understanding their various components.

Before turning to a list of the ten major breakthroughs that I expect to have a major impact on the behavioral sciences in the next fifty years, two points already touched on above require some elaboration.

Note, first, that these breakthroughs are not all, or even primarily, in the behavioral sciences per se. Discoveries about computers and mind-affecting drugs are certainly social in their significance, no matter to what discipline they owe their origin. Note, second, that we are talking about advances in behavioral *technology,* by which we mean something broader than advances in behavioral *science.*

An advance in technology may, for example, be the diffusion of something long since discovered; the steps by which the telephone was made available to millions of homes and offices represent a technological, not a scientific, advance. Freud's recognition of the unconscious was a step in the advance of behavioral *science*. Psychotherapy, group dynamics, and other similar techniques represent a related advance in behavioral *technology*.

In the natural sciences, such professions as medicine and engineering exist to put into practice the technological insights afforded by the pure sciences. In the behavioral sciences, the relation of the basic to the applied scientific disciplines is not as well developed. Applied professions such as social work, teaching, management, and diplomacy exist in the behavioral field. But the training for these disciplines, and therefore the practice of them, is much less science-based than in the natural science fields. A doctor studies intensively in natural science for three years; so does an engineer. A teacher gets at best a smattering of psychology; a management student, a few courses in economics and a casual introduction to the other social sciences; a diplomat, a touch of history, political science, and economics. There is every reason to believe that by the end of fifty years these behavioral engineering fields will require their practitioners to have the same close relation to behavioral scientists as an engineer today does to a natural scientist.

The Major Breakthroughs

Let us now list some of the changes in behavioral technology that, over the next half-century, will increase our power to conrtol social forces and will thereby make both our daily lives and our relations with the rest of the world very different from what they are today.

A Greater Use of Social Statistics

By 2018 social indicators will be as widely used as economic indicators are today. Now, the government compiles a cost of living index and the unemployment rate; Dow Jones calculates the stock market averages. A significant change in any of these makes a front-page story in *The New York Times* and swings the Federal Reserve Board, the President's Council of Economic Advisers, and even Congress into action. In countries throughout the world, estimates of the gross national product are compiled every year, and the comparative rates of growth of the communist and capitalist, underdeveloped and developed nations also make front-page news and sometimes Presidential campaign issues.

Very few social statistics are collected as regularly and studied as closely as these economic indices. The population growth rate is one such series and has been for a century. For the past twenty years, public attitudes toward the administration in Washington, as reported by the Gallup Poll, have been another social indicator, and a useful one.

By 2018 there will be many more social indicators. We will have regularly compiled indices of public happiness, broken down into such groupings as men and women, young and old, Negro and white. We will have periodic reports on the levels of public knowledge, and even monthly statistics on traffic delays. In short, we will be compiling hard and regular statistics to evaluate every important aspect of our society's performance.

Where will these statistics come from? Some will be collected by sample surveys, but most will be the by-products of normal day-to-day occurrences. For example, electronically controlled traffic lights can be wired to record data on the flow of traffic. Computer-filed samples of the symptoms patients report to their doctors all over the country can provide measures of tension and psychoneurotic reactions.

Huge Computerized Information Files

Widespread use of social indicators thus depends on another breakthrough in behavioral technology, the development of large-scale *computerized data systems*. By 2018 it will be cheaper to store information in a computer bank than on paper; files will be computer-stored and fantastically manipulative. We have already seen the beginning of this trend reflected in the public alarm about a national data center. The alarm is over the issue of privacy. All of us have many records filed somewhere: tax returns, social security records, census forms, military records, perhaps a criminal record, hospital records, security clearance files, school transcripts, and, if we include nongovernmental files, bank statements, credit ratings, job records. All of them will be stored in computer memories, easy and efficient of access and connected to each other by telephone wires.

For the behavioral sciences, this will be a remarkable breakthrough. By 2018 the researcher sitting at his console will be able to compile a cross-tabulation of consumer purchases (from store records) by people of low IQ (from school records) who have an unemployed member of the family (from social security records). That is, he will have the technological capability to do this. Will he have the legal right? This is not the place to speculate about how society will achieve a balance between its desire for knowledge and its desire for privacy. Suffice it here to note that the computer management of massive files is one of the powers technology will give us in the next half century.

Complex Model Simulations by Computer

Computers will permit us to simulate exceedingly complex systems of the many variables of which society and its component organizations are constituted. By 2018, therefore, planners will be able to experiment on computer models, testing out in advance the consequences of various policies. For example, simulation models of a city will permit the planner to build a renewal project in his imagination and foresee its probable consequences. How many people will move where? What will be the effect on rents, taxes, shopping patterns, traffic, crime rates? The planner will work with his model, changing first one detail and then another in an effort to achieve the optimum result.

A Mathematics of Relations

Between now and 2018, progress in the mathematics of systems will be of great benefit to behavioral scientists. For the past century, social scientists have for the most part confined themselves mathematically to statistics, which are primarily concerned with the frequency of occurrence of more or less independent events. It is a useful mathematics for keeping track of one, two, or a number of series. But what the social sciences increasingly need is a mathematics of relations.

One example is the mathematics of communication: If a rumor starts spreading among friends in a certain group, how far will it get how fast? Another example is systems analysis, with the need to estimate what a given set of inputs will do to the outputs. Still another is the problem of educational planning in a developing country. There are many skills for which people can be trained, and many skills the country's economy needs. To arrive at an optimum program, one must be able to calculate the possible consequences on the labor market, on the rest of the educational system, on the social structure, and so on. This is a systems problem.

Solving the Thinking and Learning Processes

By 2018 some of the mysterious workings of the human mind will have been fathomed by psychologists. Models of the learning and thinking processes will have been developed that will successfully explain many facets of human cognition. We will begin to understand how a baby learns to see and hear, how an adult brings back long-forgotten memories from the unconscious, why one person learns to read easily and another cannot, how we associate from one thought to another, how we create categories in the mind, what distinguishes the human brain from that of animals.

The impact on education of such understanding of the cognitive processes will be profound. Rates of teaching and learning will be accelerated and absorption increased. Educational technology, in the form of computerized teaching devices, audiovisual displays, and feedback devices, will become as big an industry as publishing is today.

Computers Will Talk in Sentences

Perhaps the most complex cognitive process that will have been analyzed by 2018 is language. We will long since have learned how to program computers to put grammatical sentences together in meaningful response to verbal questions, and to translate these sentences into other languages if so desired. These capabilities will be more than tricks; they will mean that we have mastered the structure of human language. In the process, we will also have learned something about the mental processes that enable humans to form statements, interpret language, and learn to talk at all. This will enable us to develop much more effective methods for language teaching and language learning, matters that will be of great practical concern in the interdependent world of 2018.

New Drugs Will Be Able to Control the Mind

Drugs that affect the mind will be much better understood half a century from now. We will have more, and more powerful, drugs, capable of making men gay or sad, suicidal or ecstatic. Some drugs will open up the gates of memory and speech; others will lock men in darkness. How society will use and control these drugs is another matter. We may become more tolerant of their use, or we may retreat from them in fear. We will not, however, be able to escape the problem. The drugs will be with us, to use well or poorly, as we choose.

More Will Be Known of Child Development

With the increased knowledge of cognitive processes will come a better understanding of how children mature. We will have some sure insights, by 2018, into what kind of man we are producing when we beat a child, or pamper him, at the age of two or at the age of twelve. We will know exactly what difference it makes for children to be spaced two years apart rather than five, what the results will be if we stuff them or starve them. We will know more about what a child carries with him in his genes and what he learns as a result of his parents' behavior. This progress in genetic psychology will, of course, have a deep impact on adult behavior. Half a century is probably not long enough to effect any dramatic change in the patterns of family life and parental responsibility. But by 2018 child rearing will be the subject of ever more intense debate, because of our heightened consciousness of the consequences of parental behavior.

People Will Lose More Inhibitions

Over the past half-century, one of the most striking trends in behavioral technology has been our growing frankness in facing our unconscious. The obvious instance is the acceptance of psychoanalysis in therapy, on the stage, in fiction, and in our daily perceptions of ourselves and our neighbors. Miniskirts, bikinis, the use of four-letter words, the hippie movement, and the spread of progressive education are other evidences of a massive loosening of inhibitions on all human impulses save that toward violence, which, on the contrary, is being ever more restricted. "Flower children" with long hair are satyr-like caricatures of the rest of us. There is every reason to believe that this trend will continue, and that by the year 2018 people will be still more uninhibited than now in openly avowing their impulses and feelings toward others and in acting out these feelings in public.

A willingness to confront one's impulses and feelings lies at the heart of more kinds of behavioral technology than just psychotherapy. Group dynamics, for example, seeks to improve human relations within organizations by having the members of a group openly avow their reactions to each other. By 2018, people will far more openly explore the feelings between bosses and subordinates, family tensions and disloyalties, their private motivations. With better understanding of the mechanics of such motivations will come a greater variety of forums in which these feelings can be frankly expressed.

Nations Will Regulate Economic Growth

Finally, an important advance in behavioral technology will be our ability, by 2018, to choose a rate of economic growth (up to about 6 percent per annum) and to hold steadily to that rate without unscheduled fluctuations. Thanks to Keynes, we have already come a long way, since the 1930's, from an errant economy swooping through uncontrolled cycles toward an economy modulated and controlled as a matter of government policy. Well before another fifty years have passed, effective control will be routine, not only in the advanced industrial countries of the West but in a large part of the underdeveloped world. Nations will make conscious choices among growth, consumption, and leisure. They will select their levels of employment, of industrialization, of increase in GNP. The choice may not be easy; parties are likely to divide bitterly in their advocacy of indulgence or investment. But, once the political decision has been made, we will have the technology to implement it.

The Waning of Nationalism

These ten developments in behavioral technology can be predicted with fair confidence, if not with absolute certainty. Far less predictable are their implications for the conduct of world affairs. How these trends apply will be critically dependent on the context in which they operate. Will the year 2018 still see a world of nation states? Will there still be only two great powers? Will industrial development still be a monopoly of the few and underdevelopment the destiny of the many? Will nuclear weapons still be poised in a delicate balance of terror, and how many nations will have them? Will the United Nations be stronger or weaker? The answers to these questions will be affected only slightly by breakthroughs in behavioral technology. Rather these contextual conditions are mostly exogenous variables that will shape the world in which behavioral technology operates.

However, the causal process does to some degree go both ways. The answers to some of these questions are partially foreshadowed in certain of the trends noted above. Specifically, we can predict that by the year 2018 the economic gap between developed and underdeveloped nations will have been narrowed, though still far from closed. With rates of growth a matter of deliberate choice for government planners, the prediction of relative growth rates will rest on the study of men's motivations and desires rather than on an analysis of blind economic forces.

There is every reason to believe that a rich and powerful nation, specifically the United States, would react with fear if any other nation, particularly a potential foe, seemed to be getting ahead of it. This nation will therefore push investment high enough to keep its leadership intact. On the other hand, until a rival appears to threaten, the United States and other wealthy nations may be expected to buy leisure ahead of rapid growth. At the same time, countries where underdevelopment is a pathology will strive — and will be helped — to narrow the gap. It will probably be well toward the year 2000 before this situation is clearly visible, for it rests upon a degree of economic control that is not yet possible. But by 2018 I would expect an optimistic answer to the question of whether the underdeveloped world will ever become modernized.

So, too, by the year 2018 nationalism should be a waning force in the world. The increasing openness about feelings and identifications may help men to overcome some of the more destructive and hostile motivations that underlie nationalism. In the coming half-century, the world has a lot of nationalistic bitterness to live down before better communication, easier translation, and greater understanding of the nature of human motivations make it common for people to react to each other as human to human, across ethnic and national lines. We can already see the beginnings of the decline of nationalism in Europe, and there is reason to believe that ultimately the decline will spread throughout the world.

One can also predict that cooperation among nations, and within international organizations, will be strengthened by the growing practice of large-scale cooperative planning. Whether the project be a communications satellite system, desalination, or antimissile area defense, the problems of scale will require planners from many nations to work together in the computerized planning process and on multinational implementation.

The Use of Computers in Diplomacy

Finally, let us look at the daily routine of the diplomat of 2018. First of all, one notes that he will be in constant, instantaneous contact with his home office, which will be served by a vast computerized information system incorporating all of its intelligence files. The U.S. State Department at present receives an average of 2,000 cables a day, and makes an average of 70 copies of each one. To help control the sea of paper, the department is now installing a computer-based retrieval system to store the cables for sixty days. But that is only the first step. Within fifty years, the total flow and backlog of the world press, monitor reports, cables, biographical and other documents will all be accessible on demand at the desk officer's console.

Perhaps the most important change for diplomacy conducted under such circumstances is that the scientifically trained technician will gradually take over from the generalist of the foreign service. We have mentioned the desk officer at his console, and alongside him will be a member of the new breed of specialists who knows how to use the data bank, with its masses of social indicators, to experiment on-line with alternate strategies by means of simulation models of the international system.

Let us be clear that the computer will not be taking over diplomacy. The computer is a tool that for the first time makes it possible for the scientifically trained analyst to bring masses of data to bear on today's problems today, and arrive at immediate answers based on tests and measurements. One advantage that the man of intuition used to have was speed. When a new cabinet was appointed in France, or a Kremlin leader made a speech, the experienced political analyst could give his interpretation at once. The man using scientific methods could not. But suppose that by 2018 a statistical analysis of the new cabinet, based on the ministers' biographies and compared to other possible cabinets, could be produced in five minutes. Or that the themes of a Kremlin speech could be compared to the themes of a dozen others in the same short time. Clearly the man trained to produce these validated analyses promptly is in a position to acquire a great deal of power in the diplomatic process, as compared to the man whose only tool is his intuition.

Finally, despite our predictions about drugs, greater understanding of cognitive processes, and improved techniques of persuasion, we have no intention of predicting that hidden persuaders will somehow be intruded into the diplomatic bargaining process to manipulate the parties by subtle tricks of propaganda or gamesmanship. Nor are we predicting that international understanding will be much enhanced by improved techniques of negotiation. Our increased knowledge of the psychology of belief and persuasion will no doubt give some clues to the would-be persuaders, but this is a game that two can play. The greater insights in the social sciences can prove just as effective for the intended victim of persuasion as for the persuader, just as useful to the conciliator as to the disrupter. Improved behavioral technology in the field of persuasion may well increase the sophistication of the bargaining process, but not necessarily to the advantage of one side over the other.

CHAPTER 8

COMPUTER TECHNOLOGY

Machines Will Do More of Man's Work, But Will Force Man To Think More Logically

by Charles R. DeCarlo

The computer, the physical realization of the joint process of logical thought and remembrance, has become in its few short years of life the symbol for an age. It is the culmination of a way of viewing the world that had its genesis in Greece and became the foundation for Western thought and science. Today the computer's conceptual basis and its technological implementation force on its users an intensification of scientific and quantitative viewpoints, leading to the agglomeration of powerful techniques that feed on each other to shape a totally new kind of environment — the so-called technological order. This process has been most intense in the materialistic "advanced" Western nations, particularly the United States.

It is likely that current concerns for the future, manifested in so many studies, are related to the existence of the new techniques brought about by computer technology in diverse fields. Because rational technique is indeed causing rapid technological change and permitting a certain

Charles R. DeCarlo, who holds a doctoral degree in mathematics, is Director of Automation Research at the International Business Machines Corporation. He is co-author of Education in Business and Industry.

amount of prediction in many sectors of human affairs, such as production, research and development, office work, intelligence, and government operations, it is natural to question how the complex of institutions embracing these activities will be related in the future. As background for such questioning, I will examine the nature of computer and communication technologies and their possible extensions in the next fifty years (though this may be a foolhardy thing to do). Following this, I will attempt some guesses as to the possible role such developments might play in the field of foreign policy.

Rapid Growth Will Continue

Before undertaking a discussion of the computer's nature, we might consider briefly its history. The basic ideas for a digital computer were enunciated in the 1830's by an eccentric Englishman, Charles Babbage. However, he lacked the technology to implement his ideas, and the possibility of building a true computer had to wait for almost a hundred years. (It is interesting to conjecture how the world's history might have developed if Victorian England had possessed the power of the computer.)

Although Englishmen continued their interest in logic, it fell to the United States to develop the first digital computers. In the late 1930's, at the Bell Telephone Laboratories under Dr. George Stibitz, and at Harvard under Professor Howard Aiken, supported by IBM, work was begun to produce computing machines. At about the same time Claude Shannon of Bell wrote a thesis on the likeness between switching circuits and the algebra of logic. This gave theoretical underpinnings to the field, and during the 1940's others, notably Eckert and Mauchly, began the development of machines that were ultimately to become the Univac. Also at about the same time, John Von Neumann and his associates, working on a new computer, used the idea of "stored-program" logic, an idea that has shaped the development of all digital computers.

By 1950 the computer was ready for industrial and government exploitation. At that time there were only ten or fifteen computers in use. Today there are almost 40,000 in the United States, 15,000 in Western Europe, and 3,000 in Japan. There are backlogs of about 15,000 orders in the United States and 4,000 in Europe. Within the next five years, it has been estimated, there will be 85,000 such machines installed. In the United States, the computer industry had an output in 1965 valued at $3.8

billion, with expectations of doubling this rate by 1970. In 1965, computers represented 8 percent of new plant investment, valued in excess of $8 billion. This figure is expected to rise to $30 billion by 1975.

But perhaps more significant than dollars or rates of growth are the increase in performance and the range of applications that have developed over the same time span. It appears that the computer is beginning to touch almost every aspect of life in the United States: medicine, education, government, industry, finance, even entertainment. With respect to performance, if we take as a measure of capacity the ratio of memory size and the speed of processing, we can assert that, beginning with the machines of 1940, there has been a thousandfold increase every ten years. In 1950 capacity had increased by a factor of a thousand over 1940 levels; in 1960 by a factor of a million; and by 1970 it is expected to increase by a factor of a billion.

These almost unbelievable increases reflect the advances in speed and size of storage and advances in computer switching, all of which decrease the time to perform a single computer operation. Yet, as we shall see, these technological advances have not been translated into equivalent practical gains in performance of the computer system, with the possible exception of certain types of scientific calculation. The reasons for this are of importance when we consider the future projections of computer technology.

Man's Senses Extended

But now let us look at the nature of the computer. Perhaps the best way to approach an understanding of the computer is to consider it, along with communication technology, as an extension of man's senses and his reasoning ability. If we do so, we will see that these new technologies of communication and control have changed, and are changing, the way time and experience are available to men. Man himself becomes a different phenomenon, seemingly capable not only of controlling the present environment but also, in a large measure, of determining its future.

Man perceives his environment essentially through his five senses. These senses enable him to communicate with other men and — largely through the amplification of his sense of touch — with his physical environment. We can observe that there is a *pair* of direct linkages in these acts of communication: between the ear and mouth, and between the eye and finger. In the case of the former, the mechanical air acts as the transmitting medium for messages from sender to receiver. Speech is the attribute that philosophers, particularly Descartes, have associated with man's human and/or divine nature. Language and speech enable the process of thought to soar to higher levels than the mere recognition of shifting patterns — a type of mental process apparently available in many of the lowest forms of life.

We can speculate on how this capacity evolved. At one time man's ancestors must have howled through the forests and by primitive sounds maintained the beginnings of pack or social cohesiveness. After millions of years, the mouth's construction evolved to the intricate mechanics of the consonant. And the consonant became interposed in the open-throated vowel voices. Words were born, and words could be used to name things — things that represented experience and commonly held meaning. Primitive action words, which held implicit in them the notion of time, also appeared, enabling communication that ranged over the present and future. To point and warn, and to name the act, was to invent a sense of future; the past remained myth and insecure memory. Men probably invented the near-future tense long before they had words to hold the past.

Jumping ahead centuries, the telephone and radio are techniques whereby this process can allow the communicants to be widely separated in space, with the illusion of language as the connecting medium. One can now communicate with the many. (What is communicated, of course, intimately depends on the shared experience between, and among, senders and receivers.) Some believe that the existence of the radio was a principal agent in Hitler's rise to power, bringing the rage of his words and the mystique of his personality to millions. In a similar fashion, the portable transistor radio today directly affects political scenes in isolated and newly emergent nations.

One of the limiting factors in the technology of communication is the availability of channels to carry all the messages men want to transmit. Recent researchers show that it is possible, by analyzing the message (for example, human speech), to transmit only a small part of the original message through the line or channel. Technological improvement in the short-range future will permit the compression of information, enabling the same communication channels to carry much more information. Computers at the sending end can analyze speech and other intelligence, reducing the signal to a small part of its original "size." At the receiving end, the computer can reassemble the information, presenting a faithful copy of the original message. This, coupled with satellite and laser communication, promises to interconnect the entire world in a massive communication net.

Next, consider the less obvious linkage between the eye and the finger. The eye perceives images from an environment that is shaped and changed largely through the agency of the fingers (or their extension by power amplifiers). The eye and brain working together enable the mind to control the apprehension of reality through touch — the fingers and their extensions.

If we return in time to the beginning of written language, we can guess the importance of this intimate connection between eye and finger to the development of human communication. The fingers traced out images, which represented names and actions. These, in turn, could be read by the eye, coordinated in the mind with the mouth-ear linkage, and, on the basis of shared experience and meaning, enable communication. The fingers could thus catch time and hold it in picture-symbols — documented history could now begin, the past made available in establishing the uses of the present. The alphabet, which reduced ideograph or pictograph to expressions of generalized units, enabled the building of flexible, rich languages.

Let's again jump ahead centuries. Now we have television, which can transmit the image, both symbolic and "real," to a distant receiver. We have the telegraph and other key-driven devices by which we can transmit coded signals that, at the receiving end, cause the "fingers" of a typewriter to move and duplicate the message. Furthermore, this technology is subject to a common discipline — communications theory — which allows us to design systems that will perceive, transmit, and recreate phenomena over large distances with predetermined reliability and fidelity. This separation has actually made the world of lived experience smaller, because more people are involved who can develop wider areas of common meaning and can move toward homogeneous cultural attitudes.

There will be startling developments in extending and deepening such communication. A quick look into the future is given in the following, taken from *The Kaiser Aluminum News*, which devoted six issues to the problems of change:

101

Let us imagine a particular space and time circa 1986: a home in the suburbs of Phoenix. A man is sitting in the middle of a circular room and on the curved walls around him he can see the ocean — surf breaking over the rocks and foaming up the beach; a fish hawk trembling in the luminescent sky. Across from him sits another man, and the two of them are talking to each other. Once in awhile, the boom of the bursting surf and the cry of the hawk intrude upon their conversation.

Let us now say that the room is underground and has no "real" view at all; that what is experienced on the curved walls is an image on a "flat wall" television screen, prerecorded in Hawaii, and now being replayed electronically. Let us further say that the first man is "real," but that the second man is being broadcast by laser beam from a satellite and recreated, in color and full dimension (you could walk around his image and see the back of his head) by "holography" so that though he is "there" in Phoenix at the moment, he is "in reality" at the same moment sitting in his study at the University of Edinburgh.

Where, in this situation, does "reality" begin and end? This will be a question that — by 1986 — we will, individually, be asked to answer. There is nothing in this situation just described that does not appear to be perfectly feasible within perhaps the next ten years; certainly within the next twenty. We have already entered a new world of experience.

The Past Will Be Vicariously Experienced

Now we shall turn our attention to another technology — that of storing or "remembering" experience. In the context of the ear-mouth linkage, we are all aware of disks and tapes. To have recorded the voices of Churchill, Dylan Thomas, John F. Kennedy, Flagstad, and Melchior enables us to recreate part of the past. In a sense we are at the beginning of a time when people will be able to choose past history that they may wish to experience vicariously through technology.

But more dramatic developments lie in the eye-finger linkage and in the design of total coordinated machine-senses systems. Such developments cannot come too quickly, for we know the difficulties associated with information storage — for example, the loss of much of the early-movie libraries. But now magnetic storage, tape, disks, and microfilms offer a potential for unlimited and almost timeless storage of experience. With the technique of computers and magnetic digital storage, it will always be possible to recreate the original recording of the experience in fresh media. This suggests a future that will have a totally new way of looking at the past and, therefore, at its own present and future. T. S. Eliot's lines on the oneness and immediacy of the present,

> Time present and time past,
> Are both perhaps present in time future,
> And time future contained in time past

take on deeper meaning against this technological background.

Having the power to transmit experience and phenomena, and to capture them in flight through storage and "remembering" technologies, constitutes an enormous jump in man's perception of time and his involvement therein. The fact that these technologies are based on motions that are measurable in billionths of a second enables them to present to us the illusion of reality — inasmuch as *our* senses operate in terms of thousandths of a second. Thus, the electronic environment will become increasingly an environment of illusion, with shifting selectivity of time and space. Already the tricks and magic that can be done with electronic tape recording and transmission enable us to "back up" time in football viewing, to see concurrently images drawn from a different space and a different time, all mixed into one stream of electronic signals that are assembled at high speed before our slow and synthesizing senses. As a matter of fact, research now shows a lag between our own "senses" and our "conscious perception" of them — a lag that is measured in the thousandths of a second. Thus, in our reality, we are always perceiving events that are already past.

These impedance mismatches between our senses and our conscious awareness, between our senses and our technologies, permit the creation of new levels of illusion and sensation. Looking ahead, we can conjecture not only the capture of time past, but also its recreation through all the senses. Technically speaking, Aldous Huxley's *Brave New World* is a primitive study.

The Possibilities Are Unlimited

So it is easy to understand that if one attempts to extrapolate into the next fifty years the development trends in memory and communication technologies of the last twenty-five years, he is faced with awesome possibilities.

First, the volume of information that can be electronically sensed, stored, and made available to the mind and senses will be increased beyond our present imagination. And not only will the information be what we normally associate with books, libraries, and film, but it will also include the storage of "total" sensory recording, such as the "laser" scene described earlier, a scene in which three different "realities" were involved. In the future it is certain that the individual will have available a great range of sensations and experiences that can be recreated for him.

Second, the development of very small, portable storage units would permit an individual to have, for his individual ownership and use, specific kinds of competencies and experience. Instead of *How to* books, he might have the actual "presence" of experts to teach and direct him. One thing is certain: Learning and education will be completely changed by the existence of such devices. Moreover, the devices could be connected to central banks of experience, permitting the individual to tap an unlimited amount of assistance and experience.

Third, the development of better input/output devices will make recorded experience more directly accessible to the "senses." Communication into the machine through modified spoken languages, by stylized writing and codification, will make the power of electronic technologies available to persons of all educational levels without specialized training. Output will be such that the eye, ear, and sense of touch will be more immediately involved, evolving a milieu of much closer man-machine interrelationships.

Finally, the flood of information generated will force the development of new ways of organizing human knowledge and experience. During the next fifty years technology will have a strong impact on the way in which language is used and on the way scholars, businessmen, government officials, and indeed everyone will think and communicate their thoughts. For we will have to organize our thinking and work so that it can take advantage of the storage, the processing, and the transmitting powers of information systems. And as the world is made smaller through communication, there will develop a "common" language, both at the technology level and at the user's level — very likely a modified and expanded form of English.

In addition to the hardware technologies of storage and transmission, there is a final aspect of technology that will contribute to man's ability to create new experience from information. This is the ability to transform and process language by means of the computer's logic.

We can consider all recorded information as a kind of language, or code, subject to being described by clusters of language. We can change such information by operating on it with well-defined rules of reason. If we confine ourselves to Aristotelian logic, the logic of decision, then *any* process or procedure that has its basis in such logic can be applied to the information representing past experience. We are thus able to reshape and manipulate basic information, ultimately restoring it through high-speed output devices to the human senses as a current experience.

In their basic conceptual form, all digital computers have a small set of operators (for example, adding, multiplying, comparing, reading, and writing) that can act on the information stored in their memories. We can imagine each individual unit of information stored in the memory as the "name" of a particular fact or "experience" (for example, earnings records, temperature readings, and logistical quantities). The computer transforms information by the sequential application of a specific operator to a specific unit of information stored in a particular cell of memory. These sequences appear as a long list of imperative sentences, each made up of an operator and "name"; or, putting it another way, of a "verb" and "noun." (For example, if we imagine storing a man's salary rate in a memory cell numbered 101, then such a sentence might be written "Multiply by 101." This has the effect of applying the "operator" or "verb" *multiply* to a number representing a particular fact about a man's earnings calculations.) An imperative sentence is called an *instruction* and the long lists of sentences are called *programs*.

Because programs themselves are information, they can be stored in memory and other programs can be used to modify them. The machine can thus alter its own sequences of sentences. This is the basic power of the "stored-program" computer.

Today programming is an arduous task, almost an art rather than a science. But many developments have taken place in the last ten years that give promise of striking changes in the future. Earlier we commented that advances in computer hardware technology had not been translated directly into comparable "practical" gains of the same order. The reason for this is that programming has not advanced at the same rate as hardware, nor has the connection of sensory input/ouput devices developed to keep pace with either.

Smaller, More 'Humanized' Machines

We may expect some startling developments in the next fifty years. We will see the creation of "self-repairing machines." Because the sequences of sentences that make up programs may involve billions of pieces of information, each of which must be executed with absolute reliability, the problem of overall system reliability is a difficult one. "Self-repairing machines" will permit the reliable use of machines in virtually any situation.

There will be the development of "self-organizing machines" — systems that can make efficient use of many components, organizing them in different ways to handle different problems. Related to this will be the development of systems that can "learn" from their own "experience," growing more capable as they are used in particular applications. This, in turn, will make machines easier to use, because the machine can take upon itself much of the burden of translating between the language used by the person and the electronic language of the machine.

Digital machines will be combined with other types of computers, such as analogue machines. This will enable the design of systems for directly controlling transformations of the physical environment, with the total system capable of learning new programs and imitating the behavior of other machines or of the human being who will "teach" the system.

The size of machines can be expected to get smaller for certain uses. Portable machines will be capable of being connected to communication systems in order to take advantage of centrally stored information and programs. Also, we can expect the "growing" of certain components of the machine and its memories. Both chemical and organic means will be used to expand the size of storage and the speed of the basic logic of the system, while reducing physical size. The use of such miniaturized machines will be of great value in prosthetic medicine and education.

The Accent Will Be on Logic

But perhaps the greatest change in the next fifty years will be in the way we look at the world — the world of both the physical and the human. For developments in memory storage, communication, and computers all weave together to make the power of rationalization more attractive and more pervasive. Even now men are increasingly thinking of their activities, environments, and relationships in terms of rationalistic patterns as being the highest *desiderata*. It is in this respect that the computer looms as handmaiden to the rational scientific approach to human affairs.

However, because systems deal only with logical chains of cause and effect, they can explore, classify, double back, and modify only within the constricted field of those processes that have been assumed, a priori, susceptible to analysis. But analysis is the breaking down and apart of process, of removing the enveloping form, of dealing with less than the whole. Using the tools of analysis with complete faith in the supremacy of reason, and in the belief that the laws of nature and man can be revealed in terms of reason (which includes mathematical, physical, and statistical foundations), the inner form of reality can be expressed in analogous systems of logic. It was this stunning realization of the power of reason and analysis, considered separately from the senses and the spirit, that truly marked the beginning of the modern world and the birth of the technical society. We refer to this separation of the world as Cartesian Dualism.

This dualism aids the separation of the domains of mind and matter, of form and content. Descartes' rejection of the idea of nature having feelings of love, suffering, and purpose, ascribing these to the God-given spirit, enabled the direct application of reason as the key to understanding and transforming the world. However, he did postulate that man was existent in the domains of both spirit and matter. Interestingly, Descartes believed speech and language, possessed by man but not animals, was an evidence of man's spirituality. This is ironic in the light of recent research in which rationalistic technique is being turned upon language and communication to analyze their nature and duplicate their processes.

A practical parallel to acceptance of this dualism is Newton's concept of the world as a large machine, operating under knowable laws. This concept determined the shape of thought in the following centuries. And the coloration from the ordered scientific world of the physical soon found its way into the world of human affairs. In suggesting an extension of such thinking, Immanuel Kant remarked that a Newton or Leibnitz was needed to discover the laws of human nature. And, indeed, the foundations of sociology, psychology, and other behavioral sciences are all rooted in the enlightened age that followed the ferment of the Age of Reason.

107

Today in the behavioral, life, and physical sciences there are many instances of intricate rational techniques that strip purpose from function, form from content. A partial list would include the analysis of work into functions, with the result that human participation in the process is now in terms of man's parts or functions rather than his totality; the analysis and explication of sexual response in which content and function, rather than form or purpose, are the overriding considerations; the analysis of behavior, both by direct implant of instrumentation in the brain and by conditioned environments; the development of learning theories in which logical information systems will play key roles as they are implemented; the modeling of systems of men and machines on the basis of statistical laws and rational procedures, as in the development of long-range plans and defense strategies; and the use of information systems in the management of business and economic enterprise in which models are established for purposes of planning and control, often with the result that a kind of self-fulfilling stability is achieved in the social and economic ecologies.

Many believe the application of rational technique, particularly the intensity with which it has been applied in this century, has wrought deep changes in man's three fundamental relationships.

First, it has changed man's relationship to man, altering family, city, state, and world relationships. In its pervasive growth, it affects the transmission of value and purpose, the process of education, and the quality of life.

Second, the rational technique has changed man's relationship to things. It has changed the act of work, with all the psychological, emotional, and social implications that follow. And as technique yields the materialistic cornucopia, men are faced with ever-new demands for consumption, with being inundated by sensory stimulation, with becoming victims to "thingness."

Third, the rational technique has changed man's relationship to transcendence. Men are forced, as the power of technique and rationalization transform the world, to a reassessment of religion, ritual, and art. The continuous upgrading of educational expectancies, the increase of information in the environment, of mobility and experience, make it possible for more people to live the "examined life." But this life is by definiton existentially painful. Thus the modern dilemmas, the nihilistic art, the "failure of nerve," the falling back into the protectiveness of the oneness of the larger organization.

In summary, we can expect in the next fifty years that the rapid development of computer technology both in hardware and systems programming will lead to machines truly capable of extending man's ability for logical thought and remembrance. In the development of such technology there will be a concomitant spread of the "scientific" or "rationalistic" way of looking at the world. This will make for an even more powerful command over the resources of nature, the shaping of the physical world to our human design. There will be an increased concern with the effects of the dualism described above — a concern with the quality of life men might lead in a society increasingly made quantitative in its operation.

The United States in 2018

Let us now turn our attention to the effects that computers, communication, and rational techniques might have on the conduct of foreign affairs in the fifty years ahead. Because the United States will be a major factor in these years, we will make several assumptions concerning its future:

¶ The political and social institutions of the United States will remain flexible enough to ingest the fruits of science and technology without basic damage to its value systems. The nature of governance will remain a process, rather than moving toward rationalistic or doctrinaire ideology. Over time there will occur the rise and fall of contesting internal powers and interests, operating within a lawful and constitutional framework. Individualism will continue to be highly prized.

¶ The current issues of civil rights will be resolved without major violent upheaval. The Negro and other minorities will be assimilated in the economic process. As educational levels are raised, emotional attitudes and prejudice will be ameliorated.

¶ The United States will increase its present commanding lead in science and technology. The trends outlined in the recent O.E.C.D. report will continue; the Soviet Union and Western Europe will partly close the gap, but the African, Asian, and South American states will fall farther behind.

¶ Attitudes toward war as an effective instrument will shift; the leveling effect of atomic warfare between, and among, the strong nations will preclude its use and probably lead to some form of international control.

The difficulty of bringing to bear advanced warfare technologies under guerrilla and primitive conditions will make "brush-fire" wars unattractive. Search-and-destroy tactics will make movements of large-scale armies impossible. The oceans will return to importance as natural constraints in policy formation.

The Effect of the Computer on International Relations

Given these assumptions, the development of computer and control technologies might have the following effects (the technology, and with it the rationalistic viewpoints that are implied, acting more as background factors than as direct agents):

1. Because these technologies involve information, they will have far-reaching effects on the uses and treatment of intelligence. Enormous banks of data, coded and readily accessible for all types of analysis, will permit the examination and monitoring of activities of nations all around the globe. Because there will be reasonable parity of ability, at least among the strong nations, the value of secrecy will be diminished. Sharing of intelligence among aligned states will probably increase. Intelligence will be used more deftly as a basis for propaganda and persuasion, gaining credibility because it will be based on fact, or seeming fact. Through "scientific" computer studies and analyses, political leadership will attempt to use information and intelligence as instruments of rationale, both internally and in the conduct of relations with other states.

2. The application of planning, analysis, and simulations to the development of possible strategies and policies will be greatly expanded. The availability of more memory, better programming, and easier communication with the electronic systems will bring this kind of competency under direct control of political leadership. The adviser role of the technician and specialist, at present based on the esoterica of computers, mathematics, and logic, will be somewhat diminished. Because many governments will have computers (even if they do not develop them) and trained manpower, such multiple planning and analysis will tend to become self-fulfilling prophecies. And because of the "openness" of intelligence and the decline of secrecy's value, such plans will tend toward positions of moderation.

3. The commonality of rationalistic techniques in the planning of government positions, and the use of similar methods of analysis and programming, will foster a kind of common "policy" information ap-

proach. This will be important in the actual conduct of foreign affairs, as well as in the preparation of background thinking and attitudes.

4. Computers and communications will markedly change the nature of national defense and also the potential for aggressive action. Defense strategies will become predominant, with highly developed watching and warning systems making "normal" methods of attack prohibitive. This will be true at both the large-scale national level and at points of posssible local "brush-fire" engagements. Defense against atomic-missile attack will be concluded to be impossible, but the general agreement that no one could "win" an all-out atomic war will preclude such attacks.

5. International banking and finance will become an even more important arm of foreign-policy formation. Communication, computers, the ability to plan and predict, and the existence of international intelligence and monitoring networks will make the effects of economic policies and decisions more immediately felt.

6. The expansion of international trade, with the concomitant development of common tastes and markets, will provide major channels through which foreign policy will be effected. Common methods of production and distribution, based on accurate and far-reaching control through the use of computer and communications, will tend to a stabilization of interests — at least among the strong and "advanced" nations. Governments will have strong and intimate relations with companies or agencies that trade throughout the world. Exchange of data between industry and government will be aided by the existence of common methods of information handling and accounting.

7. The development of science, which will increasingly use rationalistic techniques and computer technology, will further the common interest of the strong nations. The scientific community will become even more "international" in its outlook. Computer programs and methods will be shared, common libraries and professional educational facilities will tend to weld together those nations that are already committed to the expansion of major programs of research and development. Environmental control, food production, space exploration, life sciences, and worldwide attacks on disease will further bring together the "rationalistic" Western powers.

8. Computers and communication technologies will deeply affect the educational policies of most governments. The use of technologies in the learning process, the availability of a new level of library service, the

ability to bring many new kinds of experience to bear in the training and retraining of people will dramatically raise the educational levels and the expectancies of most of the Western world's populations.

9. The pervasive spread of materialistic science and the desire of the world's people for a better standard of physical well-being will diminish the importance of ideological differences among nations. It is difficult to imagine a future in which situations could develop similar to those in which Soviet Marxists rejected, on ideological grounds, "Western" genetics and the value of cybernetics as scientific disciplines. Not that men will necessarily become more reasonable; it is simply that they will have to pay attention to what "works" and modify their philosophy and ideology accordingly. The facts of science, coupled with the realities of markets, will tend to shape ideologies into a common framework, rather than the other way around.

10. The existence of computers and communication technologies will present each nation with some deep problems in the internal management of their societies. The tendency of certain forms of government toward strong central control will at first seem to be strengthened by the availability of central intelligence and control mechanisms. However, the rising educational levels of the populace and the mobility of people, with the resultant exchange of ideas and attitudes, will hopefully offset this tendency. The danger seems to be primarily in the advanced nations, where there already exist sufficient data banks and organizational skills to attempt such centralization. In the underdeveloped nations, the primitive conditions of information gathering and of administrative and organizational skills make a truly centralist apparatus unlikely.

Common Interests Will Prevail

In summary, it appears that the existence of powerful rationalistic techniques and of computer and communication technologies will tend to weld together the nations of the "advanced" societies. The polarization of the world will probably accelerate as the technically and materialistically rich nations develop common interests in opposition to the relatively poor nations, which are only now emerging into the rationalistic history of the West.

Perhaps within the next fifty years the "advanced" countries can convert a modicum of their "superior" information and knowledge into a new and unconventional wisdom. The delusive fears of the past that led nations to contest for the obvious fruits of nature, instead of cooperating to extract her much richer, hidden treasure, have made of history a nightmare. The ugly and simplistic illusion of the "other side" has more often than not led to irrational and dangerous decisions as nations have tried to share the world's resources. But with the new technologies and higher educational levels, perhaps we can hope for a better future.

U Thant has remarked, "It is no longer resources that limit decisions — it is decisions that limit resources." Indeed, the greatest promise in the computer and rationalistic techniques outlined here is the ability to explore more options and decisions. However, the selection of decision and the formulation of policy, the direction of the humane use of technology, will continue to be the statesman's burden.

CHAPTER 9

ENERGY

Ample Resources Will Supply Rising Demand

by Charles A. Scarlott

How much energy will be available to us and in what forms, fifty years from now? In a field so open to major technological development, forecasts are particularly difficult. However, we can set down trends that seem obvious at present and point to a number of broad possibilities.

First, what is the outlook for the "conventional" energy sources, that is coal, petroleum, natural gas, water power, and those forms of nuclear-energy release already so well developed that they can no longer be considered "unconventional"?

Plenty of Coal But Not So Much Oil

Coal has always been the Western world's major source of energy. Coal reserves are many times greater than all other fossil-fuel reserves combined.[1] The United States has been generously endowed with enormous reserves of thick, horizontal seams, not too deeply buried — an economically recoverable supply sufficient for hundreds of years. In spite of rising use, this will still be true a half-century hence. Not all the U.S. supply is

Charles A. Scarlott is Director of the Department of Publications at the Stanford Research Institute, and also Editor of Publications for the Solar Energy Society. He formerly worked with the Westinghouse Electric Corporation, and was co-author of Energy Sources *published in 1952.*

high-quality bituminous; there are substantial quantities of sub-bituminous coals and lignite, neither of which is suitable for coking. Fortunately, however, the bituminous reserves include large amounts of coking coal.

The situation with regard to liquid petroleum is less favorable. Proved reserves have continued to increase, but just about in step with the rising annual demand. In 1947, proved reserves stood at 25.7 billion barrels; in 1965, at 39.4 billion. However, the ratio of reserves to annual production in both years remained constant for slightly more than 12 years,[2] showing that so far oil has been found — proved — at about the same rate as we use it.

The demand for liquid petroleum is rapidly rising (from 889 million barrels in 1930 to about 3,103 million barrels in 1967).[3] The difficulty and cost of finding oil are also rising. Wells are going deeper. In 1940, no wells were drilled deeper than 14,000 feet. During 1966, 552 wells were drilled to 14,000 feet or more; of these, 50 went below 20,000 feet.[4] The average depth of completed wells in 1940 was 3,056 feet; in 1966, 4,557 feet. Furthermore, the drilling cost per foot continues to rise — from $3.68 per foot in 1964 to $4.04 in 1965.[5]

On-shore or off-shore discoveries may be made of such magnitude as to greatly change the picture, but this is highly unlikely.

Petroleum can be imported at lower cost than it can be produced in the United States. However, Congress limits imports to about 25 percent of domestic production to maintain U.S. production facilities and to safeguard the nation from becoming dependent on foreign sources. By the year 2018, production of oil from petroleum wells is likely to be insufficient to meet U.S. requirements for energy in liquid form. However, because — as we shall see — oil wells are not the only source for oil, this does not necessarily mean that the supply will be inadequate to the demand.

The natural-gas situation is even less favorable than that of oil. As with oil, proved reserves have little more than kept pace with consumption. The 1965 proved reserves of natural gas were 286,470 billion cubic feet, or 17.6 times the consumption in that year.[6] The ratio of proved reserves to annual consumption has dropped steadily since 1941, when it was about 114,000 billion cubic feet — a 33-year supply. And the race between finding and using is proceeding at a more furious clip. The demand for natural gas tripled in the last two decades — from 4,900 billion cubic feet in 1946 to 16,200 billion cubic feet in 1965.

Most natural-gas discoveries are associated with oil finds, so the likelihood of enormous findings is small. One can estimate that long before this century is out, the United States will not be able to meet more than a small fraction of the demand for gaseous energy as it is produced at present. However, with natural gas as with oil, we shall see that gas sources hitherto untappable may yield to new techniques.

Aside from developing new sources of fossil fuels, there is also the possibility of making more efficient use of the fuels available. At the moment, fossil-fuel power plants are operating at a maximum efficiency of 40 percent. Through a process known as magnetohydrodynamics (or MHD), the efficiency rate may be raised to 60 percent or more. MHD calls for raising the temperature of the fuel to many thousands of degrees and turning it into an ionized plasma from which electricity can be withdrawn directly, thus obviating the customary rotating machinery. Experiments have shown the theory to be sound, but because formidable engineering problems remain unsolved, no commercial MHD plant is in operation.

Water Power of Decreasing Importance

Water power has never provided more than about 4 percent of our energy needs, and never will. The best hydroelectric sites have already been developed, and future development will not match rising energy demand. Henceforth, the proportion of energy supplied by hydroelectric installations will slowly decrease.

Nuclear Power Limited by Cost

The nuclear-energy story is less distinct. The amount of public-utility energy supplied at present by fission of the uranium atom is so small that it can scarcely be found in the percentages. However, it will come up fast. In 1966, more than half the power-generating stations on order will be nuclear-fueled. It is expected that by 1980 about 100,000 megawatts, or one-fifth of the installed capacity, will be nuclear.[7]

But after that, what? It may be that uranium-ore reserves will prove inadequate to sustain the pace. Obviously no one can predict how much uranium ore will be found. (Thorium must be considered, too, because its exposure to the reactor environment produces U^{233}, a fissionable type of uranium. However, thorium-reactor technology has not been developed.) The experience thus far in the Colorado plateau (New

Mexico, Colorado, Wyoming), the principal source of uranium, does not suggest the likelihood of discoveries of sufficient magnitude to change the basic situation.

Because the energy in nuclear fission is so concentrated — "a teacupful will run the Queen Mary across the Atlantic" — the notion is common that the total amount necessary to run the nation's power plants is trivial. This is far from the case. A medium-size (500-megawatt), pressurized-water reactor station requires at the outset 266 tons of uranium (in the form of U_3O_8).[8] About 50 tons of additional nuclear fuel are needed for each subsequent year of operation.

The United States, which is believed to have the greatest low-cost uranium reserves in the free world,[9] will not be able to import large quantities. Canada has larger amounts than we do, but of lower grade. South Africa produces some uranium in connection with gold operations. France is thought to have about 15 percent as much low-cost uranium ($5-$10 per pound U_3O_8) as the United States. Other countries of the free world have considerably smaller amounts.

In considering uranium reserves, two things must be remembered. One is that there has been comparatively little exploration for uranium-bearing ore. Most of the search has centered in New Mexico, Colorado ·and Wyoming, where outcroppings have long been observed. There is a possibility that major fields may turn up elsewhere in the United States, or at greater depths.

The second point is that it is only the high-grade ores that are thought to be limited. Uranium oxide (U_3O_8) at present costs from $5 to $6 per pound. At higher allowable mining costs, ample quantities would become available. However, nuclear power would then become less competitive, or perhaps uncompetitive, with fossil-fuel power.

If one disregards cost, there is ample uranium. There is more potential energy in the uranium in a ton of granite than is represented by a ton of coal. Extraction, however, would be costly. If necessary, uranium could be taken from seawater, which contains the element to the extent of several parts per billion.[10]

It has been estimated[11] — this is really only an educated guess — that at a cost of from $10 to $15 per pound of U_3O_8, the reserves of uranium would double; and at from $30 to $100 per pound — which would allow for mining the oil shales, the granites, and possibly the seawater — they would be several tens of times greater. Hence, our available uranium is not a matter of the amount in the earth, but of the price we are willing to pay for it.

Breeder Reactors Provide Long-Range Hope

Natural uranium consists of several intimately mixed types or isotopes. The fissionable isotope is called U^{235}, which occurs in the ratio of only 1 part in 140 of the total uranium. More than 99 percent of the element is non-fissionable U^{238}. It is possible in a reactor to convert U^{238} to plutonium (Pu^{239}), which *is* fissionable. (Somewhat similarly, Th^{232} can be converted to the fissionable U^{235}.) This type of reactor is called a breeder, because it creates more fuel than it burns (until all the U^{238} is gone, that is).

If breeder reactors become general, our uranium fuel will be increased a hundredfold. Experts believe some breeder reactors can convert 70 percent of the U^{238} atoms to plutonium, even counting the losses due to fabrication and chemical processing.[12]

Although experimental breeder reactors have been built, no full-scale commercial units are under construction in the United States. (A few large prototypes are being built in Europe.) The engineering technology involved is vastly more difficult than is required for conventional, first-generation reactors that are cooled by ordinary water, heavy water, or gas under pressure.

Breeder reactors are not expected to come into major use before the 1980's. By that time the supply of low-cost uranium may be getting low. However, there is little doubt that the engineering problems posed by breeder reactors will be solved and that they will be in extensive use long before fifty years go by.

Solar Energy — Inventive Breakthrough Needed

The daily rain of solar energy is immense by any measure. The amount falling on the United States is several thousand times the amount of energy that the nation consumes. The problem, however, is to "catch" the energy, which, although great in total, is diffuse. On a clear day at noon, the solar radiation falling on a square meter of surface amounts to about one kilowatt. The low efficiency (about 15 percent maximum) of power-collection devices and the variability of sunshine (down to zero at night and very little on cloudy days) have so far rendered solar energy ineffectual for major power purposes.

What is needed is some inexpensive and efficient means for converting radiant energy into a useful energy form, such as electricity, and a vastly better method of energy storage. These are more possibilities than probabilities. Silicon solar cells range from 6 to 15 percent efficient, with any great improvement believed impossible. Also, the more efficient silicon-type cells are expensive — about $50,000 per kilowatt. The cadmium-sulfide cell is less expensive but is even less efficient. As to storage devices, an improvement of at least tenfold is needed.

Solar energy is extremely valuable, and will become more so for many localized, limited-power applications. However, we cannot expect that sunshine will take over a significant portion of the energy load in another half-century.

One reservation must be made. Should devices be invented that convert sunshine into electricity more efficiently at low cost, and *if* much better and inexpensive energy storage becomes available, we can expect many homes to have their own power plants. In any case, we can reasonably foresee that a large number of homes will be heated and cooled by solar energy through systems designed to capture the sun's heat in water. Nevertheless, such developments at most would do no more than to reduce, somewhat, the *rate of increase* of energy demand.

Solar energy is well adapted to small-quantity production (a few kilowatts) for local use. This makes it a good candidate for heating, cooking, water pumping, refrigeration, and communication tasks in underdeveloped countries. Solar-energy systems could thus become a significant part of the United States foreign-aid program.

Trace Sources — Inconsequential for Future

Other sources of energy are sometimes mentioned: tidal power, geothermal (earth heat), and wind. These can all be dismissed as inconsequential.

We must remember that it is possible to *grow* liquid fuel.[13] Alcohol, which can be an excellent fuel for internal combustion engines, or even an additive to gasoline, is produced from a wide variety of agricultural crops. This is a special, and inefficient, example of solar-energy conversion and storage. A ton of corn, for example, produces 84 gallons of alcohol. The cheapest fermentation alcohol would probably come from blackstrap molasses. An acre of sugar cane could provide about 280 gallons of alcohol — and do it repetitively. However, it is reasonably certain that, with the pending world food shortage, food-crop land is unlikely to be diverted to the production of fuel. Interestingly, in the 1940's, alcohol plants were built in the Dominican Republic, Jamaica, India, Brazil, and Pakistan.

Fusion —No Solution in Sight

When we speak of the energy of the future, fusion poses the largest question mark. Fusion is the basic reaction that produces the energy of the sun and of the stars. It is, indeed, the basis for all of the earth's energy (except tidal, geothermal, and nuclear energy). It is also the mechanism of the hydrogen bomb.

Essentially, in the fusion reaction, the kind of hydrogen atoms known as deuterium is "burned" to produce helium and a large amount of heat. (A pound of deuterium, if burned completely, would produce about 10 million kilowatt hours of heat.) Deuterium is the form of hydrogen found in heavy water. The ratio of deuterium and hydrogen in natural water is 1 to 6,200. But there is so much water that the amount of deuterium potentially available for fusion power plants is for all practical purposes inexhaustible. The technology of deuterium separation from water, although not inexpensive, is well developed. (Heavy water costs about $18 per pound. Deuterium would thus cost less than $100 per pound.)

The obstacle to fusion plants is not "fuel." It is fusion technology. The task of making the fusion process a controlled, continuous reaction has not been accomplished. The principal difficulty is that the fusion reaction occurs and is self-sustaining only at temperatures in the millions of degrees (at lower temperatures, the "fire" goes out). Such heat obviously presents fantastically difficult problems in connection with the construction material for the fusion furnace. All known materials become gases at temperatures far below fusion heat.

There is a way of confining the reacting gases, which are so hot that they are actually plasmas, without letting them come into contact with the furnace walls. The electrical forces present are such as to constrict the plasma within what is called a "magnetic bottle." Unfortunately, the "bottle" is inherently unstable; any imperfection or slight disturbance destroys it. Much effort has been spent on this problem, but no solution is yet in sight. To date, the maximum length of time that a continuous fusion reaction has been produced is measured in small fractions of a second. And, aside from the serious instability problem, other enormous engineering difficulties must be overcome before a practical operating fusion plant can be achieved.

Once built, such plants would be enormously efficient; energy could be extracted directly as electricity without the intervention of motion, as in a steam or nuclear-power plant. They would be extremely large — much larger than the largest of today's power plants — and would produce enormous quantities of electrical energy at extremely low cost. The fusion potential is indeed great, warranting the expenditure of large sums for research.

It seems likely that if the fusion process is to be mastered at all for practical purposes, it will be accomplished within the next fifty years. It is not too much to suggest that success would assure mankind an ample source of energy for thousands of years.

Oil Shale — A Recovery Problem

Other technological developments could change both the energy patterns and the total amounts of energy available. One is the capture of energy from oil shale. The greater part of the U.S. deposits of this material is in Colorado and Wyoming, mostly in federal lands. The deposits are enormous: it is estimated that from 250 to 750 billion barrels of oil lie locked in what is rather erroneously called shale (rock would be a better term). Assuming some reasonable degree of efficiency in recovery, even the minimum estimate would assure us a supply of petroleum a thousand times greater than our present annual consumption.

Oil can be recovered from shale; there is no doubt of that. The U.S. Bureau of Mines and several industrial companies have spent large sums in experimentation, using different methods. Oil — more precisely, kerogen — has been produced. The practical questions are those of competitive economics and which of several alternative processes is best. Even now, oil can be produced from the kerogen of shale at costs that border on the competitive with crude oil from wells.

There are problems, of course. One is the matter of utilization of the shale on government land. More serious, perhaps, is what to do with the spent shale after it has been retorted. A ton of oil shale yields about 30 gallons of oil plus nearly a ton of "ash." Disposal of this ash will be difficult. It has been estimated that if all the shale in Colorado were retorted to produce oil, enough spent shale would remain to cover the state to a depth of one foot. There are simply not enough spare canyons for disposing of these ash heaps — even if that were permissible.

This is one reason why serious attention is being given to methods of extracting the oil *in situ*. One proposal is to drill holes through the shale and set fire to the bottom in such a way that the heat converts the kerogen, which is a solid, to a liquid that could be drained into reservoirs. It has also been suggested that a nuclear blast could be set off within a shale deposit both to shatter the shale vein and, by the heat of the blast, to release the oil. Almost surely this scheme will be tried. Success cannot yet be assumed. Whether uranium can be spared for this task is another question.

Nuclear blasts are under consideration for another form of energy release. As of January, 1968, a charge of uranium equivalent to 26 kilotons of TNT was exploded in a gas well in the Leandro Canyon gas field of New Mexico (Project Gasbuggy).[14] The purpose was to shatter the rock in which the gas was locked, allowing it to escape. At this writing, the result has not been announced, but the first indications were encouraging. Success would mean the rejuvenation of many wells from which gas and oil are no longer recoverable by the usual means. How much this technique would add to our fossil-fuel reserves is pure speculation. It could range from a modest increase to something extensive.

Energy in 2018

For the first quarter of the 21st century, the energy outlook for the United States may be summarized as follows: Coal reserves will still be large. Petroleum and natural gas will probably be far short of demand, which will be three to four times greater than at present.[15] However, both liquid and gaseous energy should be available at reasonable cost from other sources, such as from oil shale, coal, or possibly — with the development of new techniques — from wells now considered uneconomic to operate. Energy from water power, solar radiation, the wind, tides, or earth heat will not figure large in the totals. Power from nuclear plants should be available in large amounts at low cost. Fusion power, still a question mark, is more likely than not to be practical and, if so, would mean a vast extension of available energy.

In a nutshell then, the United States in another half-century should continue to have ample amounts of energy at acceptable cost to meet a greatly augmented demand. This means that the nation's industrial plants will not be energy-limited or penalized by high costs (although the costs will be somewhat higher than they are today). From an energy point of view, the United States should be competitive in world markets. Importation of large quantities of energy, destructive of our balance of payments, should not be necessary. Thus, the United States supply of energy as a factor in foreign policy should not be substantially different than at present.

This is not to say that the pattern of energy use will remain the same. Already we hear that the electric automobile will return, or that the fuel-cell automobile will arrive, to alleviate air pollution. Individual solar power plants for home use may materialize. Solar air-conditioned homes are a distinct possibility. We can be sure that in the year 2018 the way we spend our energy resources will differ considerably from present patterns. But energy, however produced and used, will continue to be available at reasonable costs for greatly expanded use.

This, however, is not the whole story. Most of the United States' partners in the free world are not as abundantly blessed with energy supplies. England has coal, but the mines are deep, the seams thin, and mining costs are rising rapidly. The Ruhr area of Europe is rich in coal, but production is actually declining because Ruhr coal cannot compete either with oil imports or with coal imported from the United States. (In 1965 the United States exported to West Germany 5 million metric tons of coal, 8 million to Italy, 13 million to France, and 3.5 million to The Netherlands.) Natural gas and petroleum have been discovered in the North Sea and in The Netherlands. The full extent of these fields is not yet known, but probably they are sizable. Western Europe is not believed to have significant uranium reserves. In sum, Europe is an importer of energy and can expect to continue to be, particularly in view of rapidly growing demand.

Japan's principal native energy is water power. She already imports both coal and oil. In 1965 the United States supplied her with 6 million metric tons of coal — half of Japan's total consumption. Australia is Japan's second principal source of coal. Oil is imported from Venezuela, Indonesia, and the Arabian peninsula. Japan is not known to have significant uranium ores.

Latin America, except for Venezuela and to a lesser extent Mexico, is already energy-short; and, as the economies grow, the shortage will increase. The African nations — except for the Arab states bordering the Mediterranean, and Nigeria — are only modestly endowed with energy sources. Here the sun may have an important role as an energy source in a few decades.

Of America's principal partners in the free world, Canada and Australia have good reserves of low-cost energy sources. But where can Western Europe and Japan look for petroleum in the next few decades? The answer appears to be the Arab countries and the Soviet Union. Already the countries of Southern Europe are drawing large quantities of petroleum and liquefied natural gas from North Africa and the Middle East. More recently, it appears that the Soviet Union is preparing to provide Central Europe with both oil and natural gas; several large pipelines have been built or are under construction across the Soviet Union to the very doorstep of Western Europe. The possibility is very real that Western and Central Europe and Japan will become dependent for energy on the Soviet Union and the Arab countries. The effects on the foreign policies of countries that up to now looked to the United States for leadership can be considerable.

This situation is not something decades away. It may arise within a decade. It is but one example of shifts in energy flow on the international scene that can have a major bearing on the outlook of nations and on world leadership. We can be sure that in fifty years the demand for energy in energy-short and growing economies will have major policy implications for all countries.

There will, therefore, be increased rivalry among the industrial nations for access to the more abundant and cheaper reserves of energy, mainly petroleum. The Middle East contains about three-fourths of the known world oil reserves. This fact lends significance to the recent increase of Soviet — and to some extent, of French — influence in the oil-producing countries of that region. At present, Europe draws about 70 percent of its petroleum from the Middle East. Because oil provides a constantly increasing proportion of Europe's energy, whoever controls this major source will dominate industrial Europe. The consequences for U.S. foreign policy seem obvious.

Energy is the base of any industrial society. The safest prediction one can make in this dynamic field is that whatever the changes we predict for the year 2018, they are likely to be grossly underestimated.

NOTES

1. Henry R. Linden, "Pipeline Gas from Coal," *Coal Age,* January, 1965, p. 65.
2. "Oil Reserves Up but Not Far Above Six Years Ago," *World Oil,* Feb. 15, 1967, p. 137.
3. *Ibid.,* p. 122.
4. *Ibid.,* p. 120.
5. *Ibid.,* p. 122.
6. *Ibid.,* p. 140.
7. "Energy and Energy Movement," *Coal Age,* January, 1966, p. 110.
8. E. M. Kinderman, *Nuclear Materials Management,* a paper presented at Stanford Research Institute, Day Associates, San Francisco, Dec. 14, 1967.
9. "World Uranium and Thorium Resources," *European Nuclear Energy Agency,* Paris, August, 1965.
10. "The Outlook for Uranium," *A Report to the East Central Nuclear Group,* S. M. Stoller Associates, New York, July, 1965.
11. Kinderman, *op. cit.*
12. Kinderman, *op. cit.*
13. Eugene Ayres and C. A. Scarlott, *Energy Sources,* McGraw-Hill Book Co., New York, 1952, p. 235.
14. "Good Start for Gasbuggy," *Time,* Dec. 22, 1967.
15. Hans Landsberg, *Resources in America's Future,* Johns Hopkins Press, 1964, p. 179.

CHAPTER 10

FOOD

The World's People Won't Go Hungry

by D. Gale Johnson

With all of the uncertainty that exists with respect to the world food supply, now and in the near future, one should hesitate to look as much as five decades ahead. There are those who believe that per capita food supplies in the developing countries are less adequate than before World War II. There are others, including this writer, who believe that there has been some modest degree of improvement. There are some who believe that during the next decade famine will be widespread. Although discouraging predictions make for shocking headlines in the press and provide subjects for TV documentaries, sounder analysis fails to support these dire prognoses.

It has now become clear that the contraction of world stocks of grain that started in 1961 was due to five factors coming into play more or less simultaneously: (1) temporary and modest success of acreage-control programs in the United States; (2) a rapid growth in commercial demands for feed grains; (3) large-scale imports of grains by the Soviet Union; (4) the emergence of Communist China as a modest but sustained net importer of grain; and (5) two bad monsoons in India.

Of these factors, only the second and fourth are likely to persist for some time, and there is evidence that the growth rate in the commercial

D. Gale Johnson is Dean of the Division of the Social Sciences and professor of economics at the University of Chicago. He has served on numerous federal projects, and is currently an adviser to the Policy Planning Council of the State Department.

demand for feed grains has slowed. The fact that world grain stocks plus current production were adequate to meet all these factors coming at the same time is perhaps more astounding than that grain stocks declined in the six-year period.

Moreover, if there was famine during this period, it was not due to an actual lack of food, but rather to the internal policies and transportation and marketing limitations of the affected countries. Those who feel overwhelmed by the constant predictions of impending starvation and doom should remember that until 1966 the last major famine in the world occurred in Bengal in 1942-43 (unless there was famine in China in the early sixties). So long a time between major famines is unparalleled in modern history.

Long-Run Food Outlook Is Optimistic

There are three reasons why I am relatively optimistic about the prospects for increasing per capita food availability in the developing countries over the next half-century. These are:

1. It is now clear that the application of the relevant scientific knowledge can result in the development of food-crop varieties and methods of production that will make possible substantial increases in per acre output of food. Those of us who might be impatient with the progress made to date should remember that U.S. food-crop yields were stagnant for at least a half-century until major breakthroughs occurred in the thirties — and even these did not start to have a major effect until the early forties.

2. It is now increasingly recognized that the failure of most farmers in the developing world to adopt so-called modern methods has not been due to their ignorance, illiteracy, obstinacy, or insensitiveness to economic incentives. The now rather numerous studies of the subject, including the sorely neglected pioneering study *Penny Capitalism* by Sol Tax, and *Transforming Traditional Agriculture* by T. W. Schultz, are at last undermining much of the fuzzy thinking and misconceptions that have for so long guided national policies in a number of developing countries and influenced the aid policies of the industrial nations.

3. Research on contraception holds promise of providing techniques that will be acceptable to most of the world's population. Obviously, effective family planning depends on much more than the ready availability of cheap and effective methods of contraception. The modification

of attitudes and expectations by the users of family-planning methods, the abandonment of opposition by religious groups and by those who believe they gain by high birth rates, and increased concern with the subject at national policy-making levels are all required. The limited success that has been achieved until now should not be taken as proof that little can be done. After all, very little has been attempted.

Farmers Will Still Grow Our Food

Looking five decades ahead, I do not anticipate that any significant fraction of the world's food supply will be produced by factory methods. Barring a major scientific breakthrough not now realizable, there does not appear to be any known process that would permit the production of any important part of the world's food supply at a cost competitive with agriculture as it is now organized and evolving. Obviously, agriculture will change a great deal in the fifty years, more in some regions than in others, but except for the production of certain special elements of food, such as specific amino acids, vitamins, and trace mineral elements, most of the food consumed will be produced by processes evolved from centuries of development in farming. This will be particularly true of the food caloric base.

There are two quite simple reasons why I believe that the world will continue to depend on farming, supplemented in an important way by fishing, for most of its food supply in the decades ahead. The first is that the principal food of the world (eaten directly or through animal products), the grains, is relatively low in cost. Few products are produced at a lower cost per kilogram; the few cheaper ones are primarily minerals that are utilized with little or no processing — coal, limestone, crude salt. Two of the common grains — corn (maize) and wheat — are produced at costs of from 5 to 7 cents per kilogram; rice is produced for about 10 cents in major exporting countries. In contrast, pig iron costs about 10 cents per kilogram and automobiles about $1.25 per kilogram at the factory. In the nonagricultural sector, very few products are produced at a lower cost per unit of weight than pig iron and many cost much more than automobiles.

The second reason is the enormous *weight* of food that is produced each year. In order to supply the calories required for life, it appears that there is little possibility of reducing the dry weight involved. U.S. grain production, measured by weight, is more than 1.5 times greater than steel and 10 times greater than automobiles. The current low cost of food grains — the major primary or secondary source of calories for all people — combined with the enormous volume or weight involved make it most unlikely that much progress will be made in the next fifty years in replacing agriculture by factories.

It is my expectation that if factory methods of creating or transforming calories do emerge over the next half-century, it will not be because food has become cheap, but because it has become much more expensive relative to other products than it now is. The currently available or imagined methods of producing food in a relatively small area — and this is the main distinction between conventional and factory methods of producing food — are several times more expensive than the methods now in use.

Research Can Boost Crop Yields

Can enough food be produced by conventional means to provide for relatively adequate diets for the world's population over the next half-century? If some significant headway is made in reducing birth rates through family planning, and if the task of increasing food production is given sufficiently high priority, it is reasonable to predict that the world population in the early part of the 21st century will be significantly better fed than is today's.

Only in the last decade or two has there emerged a reasonable prospect that the developing countries could achieve increased production through higher output per unit of cultivated land rather than by increased area under cultivation. The basic reasons for the static nature of yields have been well explained by my colleague, T. W. Schultz, in his major work, *Transforming Traditional Agriculture.* At fault were neither redundant labor, inefficiency, nor laziness, but the lack of superior alternatives. Only in recent years has a serious effort been made to apply modern technology effectively to the agricultural problems of the developing countries. (We still have done little research on the production of food crops in the tropics.)

The accumulated evidence indicates quite clearly that modern science has a great deal to contribute through the development of higher yielding crops, food grains of higher quality, and better methods of cultivation and protection. I am convinced that, with appropriate effort, food-crop varieties can be developed for any region of the world that will yield from three to five times as much as the best of the existing varieties — or at least the best that existed until five years ago. The successes that have been achieved in Mexico by the Rockefeller Foundation and the Mexican government, and in the Philippines by the International Rice Research Institute, as well as other successes in Japan and Taiwan, can be duplicated elsewhere if sufficient effort is made.

The experience of recent years also shows that farmers in the developing world will adopt new varieties and new methods of production if the relevant inputs are available and if appropriate economic incentives exist. The pessimism about the intractability of the peasant, so prevalent in the forties and fifties, has proved unwarranted. The groundless pessimism arose out of a false premise — that the crop varieties and production methods of the United States, Western Europe, and Japan could be readily transferred to the developing countries. Instead of questioning the validity of these assumptions, all too many policy-makers assumed that the difficulty lay in the unwillingess of the farmers to adjust to changing conditions. It is now quite clear that the farmers were generally correct in refusing to adopt American, European, or Japanese crop varieties and methods.

Superior Crops Are Possible

One of the most promising developments of the next decade or so will be the modification of the amino-acid composition of common food crops as well as a likely increase in their protein content. Although it is true that at present there are sufficient supplies of protein — now used as livestock feed or fertilizer — to supply adequately every child and adult in the world, we have not yet been able to develop readily acceptable mechanisms for adding proteins to diets in areas where shortages exist. Although further efforts at developing special — and acceptable — high-protein foods for children and pregnant women, as well as the general population, should and will be made, the greatest chance of success probably lies in changing the protein level and composition of the common food grains and roots. The development of a greatly superior variety of corn at Purdue University is a step in this direction and opens up exciting possibilities. Although there is no assurance that a similar breakthrough is possible for each of the major food crops, the increasing sophistication of plant breeding holds out real hope that with sufficient effort, positive results can be achieved.

Cheaper Energy Will Cut Production Costs

Further developments in the generation of nuclear power hold out the likelihood that, some time in this century, the cost of electricity in the developing world will decline substantially and its general availability will be enormously increased. These developments should have a major impact on agriculture in the developing world, making possible a substantial reduction in the cost of nitrogenous fertilizers and the superphosphates.

Lower energy costs should also result in a substantial increase in the quantity of irrigated land. This will be true for at least four reasons: (1) economic desalinization of sea water requires cheap energy; (2) low-cost energy should greatly increase the utilization of subsurface water by reducing the cost of pumping; (3) there are a number of areas that could be irrigated if the cost of raising surface water could be reduced; and (4) if nuclear power should prove cheaper than hydroelectric power, some of the water required to maintain an even flow at the hydro plant would become available for irrigation. Operation of a hydro facility would become uneconomic at the moment the value of water for irrigation exceeded the difference between the current operating cost of the hydro plant and the cost of producing nuclear energy. It need not wait until the costs of nuclear power fall to the level of the current operating cost of hydro generation.

Farm Machinery Is Key to Efficiency

One of the important sources of increased food availability in the industrial nations has been the replacement of animals by mechanical power. The anticipated structure and size of farms are unlikely to make possible the introduction of medium or large tractors in much of the developing world. However, the ingenuity of the Japanese in adapting the garden tractor and developing auxiliary machinery for efficient use on farms of a hectare or less will redound to the benefit of areas with small farms before our half-century comes to an end.

Although it is impossible to project with any reasonable degree of accuracy the rate of adoption of machines because so many variables are involved, the increased use of mechanical power might provide the food for as much as a fifth or a sixth of the increase in the world's population over the next fifty years. It has been estimated that at the present time the feed requirements for animal power are approximately two-thirds of the food (in terms of energy) consumed by people. Although much animal feed is inedible by humans, a decline in animal power would permit the production of more livestock products for human consumption and the extension of plowed areas in many parts of the world.

Population Growth Must Be Curtailed

For most of the people of the world, obtaining enough food of the right kind for healthy growth has always been a major problem. The situation confronting the developing countries today is no more serious than it has been in the past. The fairly general view that the per capita supply of food will decrease in the near future is based largely on the current and unprecedented rates of population growth in the developing nations. Until these rates decline, food supply must grow at something like from 2.5 to 3 percent annually just to maintain per capita consumption.

However, it can again be said that developments in methods of contraception — and expected results from research now under way — open prospects for reducing birth rates in the foreseeable future. As in so many other areas related to food and population problems, even the rather limited research efforts so far made have already resulted in major gains. Obviously, much more needs to be done, but recent experience indicates that there is likely to be a high payoff from additional investment in research and action programs.

The Need — An Enlightened Foreign Policy

What challenges to American foreign policy are more or less implicit in the projection I have given of the world food situation for the next fifty years? I emphasize four such challenges, though some involve aspects of domestic agricultural policy as well as what is normally considered to be foreign policy.

1. Our programs to aid the agricultures of developing countries should be independent of concerns about the impact on U.S. domestic agriculture. The importance of this change in policy should not be underestimated. It should not be assumed that a fundamental change has occurred because, with one exception, the Food for Peace Act of 1966 is based on the philosophy that the United States should assist those countries that are willing to give a high priority to agricultural development. The real test will come in the battle over appropriations: Will Congress really provide the funds to assist an expansion of wheat or rice production if

this might result in a loss of U.S. grain markets? Actually, the available evidence indicates that rapid growth of agriculture in a developing country tends to increase our agricultural exports. The reason for this apparent anomaly is that rapid agricultural development is associated with general economic growth, which, in turn, results in an increase in imports of food products.

2. We must make possible long-term support of research on the problems of increasing agricultural production in the developing countries. Although almost every phase of our foreign economic-aid program is adversely affected by the unwillingness to provide support for a period in excess of a year, the procedure is especially damaging to research programs. The United States has a great deal to contribute in this field: scientists, administrators, and education facilities. But the numerous efforts that we have financed so far have had very limited payoffs, largely because of uncertainty over the duration of the commitment and the lack of patience. It should not be expected that a research program will produce major results in less than a decade; the expectation that results will come in a year or two will almost certainly be disappointed.

Our land-grant universities and the Department of Agriculture have the capacity to man major research efforts in all the principal agricultural areas of the world. The cost of mounting such an effort in as many as fifty centers for a period of two decades would be surprisingly small compared to the cost of food aid or certain other forms of economic assistance. At an average operating cost per center per decade of, say, $20 million, the total for fifty centers over two decades would be $2 billion. Capital costs would be substantial, but probably not more than half of the operating cost. Thus the total cost might be about $3 billion.

Such research efforts should be combined, of course, with the education of significant numbers of local scientists who could eventually take over the entire operation, perhaps with a transitional period of U.S. financial and technical assistance.

The first step in such a plan might be the creation of a governmental corporation provided with sufficient funds to cover all its operation costs for the two-decade period. The corporation need not be an operating agency in the usual sense of the word; its primary responsibility would be to establish priorities and enter into contracts with universities and the U.S. Department of Agriculture to create and operate the research stations in the various parts of the world. Its board of directors should include outstanding scientists who could evaluate proposals and progress as well as assist in establishing priorities. The primary requirements are for autonomy from the day-to-day operations of foreign policy, outstanding leadership and direction, and certainty of financial support for a period of time sufficiently long to permit an opportunity to engage in research that has the best chance of producing results.

3. We need to adopt trade and agricultural policies — and to induce other industrial nations to do likewise — that will permit the developing nations to export those crops in the production of which they enjoy a comparative advantage. All industrial countries protect sugar production, inefficient as that plant is to grow under temperate climatic conditions. Other products that can be produced at the lowest cost in the developing countries are also heavily protected by many industrial nations — peanuts, tree nuts, certain fruits and vegetables, and rice. Industrial nations also provide heavy protection for the first processing of many agricultural raw materials imported from the developing countries. Because many of these processes are relatively simple and often require relatively little capital, they should be performed where the products are grown.

At best, the developing countries whose chief exports are agricultural — this is true of most of them — are finding that their markets in industrial nations are growing only very slowly, if at all. This is due to the low rate of population growth in the advanced nations, as well as to the slow rate at which the per capita consumption of food rises. Clearly, certain modifications in trade and agricultural policies of the industrial nations are called for if economic growth of the less fortunate states is to be encouraged.

The developing countries will need a great deal more foreign exchange than they now earn if they are to provide the inputs required to achieve a significant increase in the rate of growth of food supply. The President's Science Advisory Committee has estimated that the investment costs of the input industries needed to double the agricultural production of the developing countries (excluding mainland China) would be about $35 billion.[1] Most of this investment is required for fertilizer production, storage, transportation, and marketing facilities. In addition, a significant part of the investment would involve foreign exchange.

Changing the trade and agricultural policies of the developed nations could easily result in an annual $1-billion increase in the foreign-exchange earnings of the developing nations. By the end of the century, such an annual increase would provide the $35 billion needed, according to the President's Science Advisory Committee, to double their agricultural yield. (I have argued elsewhere that if the Western industrial nations eliminated their protection of agriculture, the developing countries would probably be able to increase their annual exports by $2 billion.[2])

4. The United States should make it clear that it does not intend to provide long-term food aid on a major scale to any nation. This position is, of course, consistent with the Food for Peace Act of 1966, which states that by 1971 all Title I sales should be for dollars, though on relatively easy credit terms. The developing countries should be given a positive sign that we intend to carry out this provision of the act.

In saying this, I do not mean to imply that the United States should not continue to provide emergency food to meet a wide variety of disasters. Nor is there any reason why limited food aid should not be provided in connection with other forms of economic assistance. But the quantities of such aid should be consistent either with the needs of some quite specific activity, such as school lunches, or with the share of the total expenditure that would otherwise go for the importation of food. Moreover, the barter program of Title III of the Food for Peace Act is so clearly inconsistent with a liberal and nondiscriminatory trade policy that it should have long been abandoned.

NOTES

1. *The World Food Problem; a Report of the President's Science Advisory Committee, Report of the Panel on World Food Supply,* Vol. II, The White House, May, 1967, pp. 375-400.
2. D. Gale Johnson, "Agriculture and Foreign Economic Policy," *Journal of Farm Economics,* Vol. 48, No. 5 (Dec., 1964), p. 927.

CHAPTER 11

POPULATION

The World's People
Will Nearly Triple in Number

by Philip M. Hauser

The United Nations in 1966 issued population projections to the end of the century, for the world as a whole and for the economically developed and developing areas of it. The projections indicate that, if present high fertility and declining mortality rates continue, world population will reach 7.5 billion by 2000. On the contrary supposition that the birth rate *declined* along with the mortality rate, the U.N. calculated three additional projections, termed high, low, and medium variants. The high variant gives a world population in 2000 of 7 billion, the medium variant 6.1 billion, and the low 5.4 billion.[1]

Each of these variants — other than the 7.5 billion projection based on present fertility levels — assumes a decrease in birth rates in the developing areas. But it must be emphasized that up to this time there is no firm evidence, despite specific search, that reductions in the birth rate have yet occurred among the illiterate and impoverished mass populations of Asia, Latin America, and Africa. In consequence, the projection based on the continuation of present fertility rates cannot be dismissed as wholly outside the realm of possibility. Furthermore, all of the variant

Philip M. Hauser, one of the world's leading demographers, is Director of the Population Research and Training Center and professor of sociology at the University of Chicago. He has been the U.S. representative on the U.N. Population Commission and has served as an adviser on statistics to the governments of Burma and Thailand.

projections have built into them assumptions of fertility decline that currently may be more accurately described as speculative than empirically founded.

For purposes of this discussion, therefore, the high variant projection will be employed, even though the U.N. accepts its medium variant as the most probable. It should be stressed, however, that the conclusions to be reached here would not vary significantly if the medium projection were used.

On the basis of this high variant, the world's population will rise from about 3.3 billion in 1966 to 7 billion by the year 2000, a more than twofold increase. Of special economic and political import for this period is the differential in the growth rates of the developed and the developing areas. The U.N.'s high projections indicate that the less developed areas will have an aggregate population of about 5.4 billion by 2,000, whereas the more developed areas will total about 1.6 billion.

According to these projections, then, the less developed areas (1960 population: 2 billion) will increase by some 3.4 billion persons by the end of the century, or by 170 percent — an increase equivalent to the present population of the globe. In contrast, the more developed areas will increase by only 598 million persons, or by about 60 percent. Thus, the population increase in the less developed areas will be more than five times as great as in the more developed areas.

In projecting world population beyond 2000 to the year 2018, a number of alternative assumptions are, of course, possible. Population projections are fictitious models of what may transpire; the actual course of events may be quite different. To obtain population projections for the year 2018, the key assumptions employed here are the following:

1. That the high projections of the U.N. represent reasonable figures for the year 2000.[2]

2. That the impact of family planning programs will decelerate growth in the years 2000 to 2018 to the rate (geometric) of world growth implicit in the U.N.'s medium estimates for the 1965-2000 period.

These assumptions are justified by two considerations. First, they may be regarded as reasonable evaluations of the progress population control is likely to make between now and 2018 — fifty years, or about two generations, hence. Second, they permit simple and expedient calculations that for the time period involved — the eighteen years between 2000 and 2018 — are consistent with the law of parsimony.

To provide a range as against a point estimate for these years, projections also were made to obtain low and high estimates. The low projection is based on the U.N. medium population estimate for 2000, as a starting point, and on the assumption that the U.N. medium growth rate between 1965 and 2000 continues. The high projection assumes that the population in 2000 is 7.5 billion, based on the continuation of present trends in fertility and mortality, but that thereafter the U.N.'s medium growth rate obtains.

On the basis of these assumptions, the world's total population in 2018 and that of the advanced and developing areas and their major subdivisions are given in the accompanying table.

Population for the World, More Developed and Less Developed Areas, 1965, and Projected to 2000 and 2018 (Hauser Medium Estimate)

Area	Population (in millions)			Percent Distribution		
	1965	2000	2018	1965	2000	2018
World Total	3295	6994	9710	100.00	100.00	100.00
More Developed Areas[1] ..	1038	1574	1980	31.50	22.51	20.39
Europe	445	563	657	13.51	8.05	6.77
Soviet Union	231	403	532	7.01	5.76	5.48
Northern America	214	376	496	6.49	5.38	5.11
Australia and New Zealand	14	26	35	0.42	0.37	0.36
Other	134	206	260	4.07	2.95	2.67
Less Developed Areas[2] ...	2257	5420	7730	68.50	77.49	79.61
East Asia (less Japan)	756	1484	2016	22.88	21.22	20.76
South Asia	978	2443	3515	29.68	34.93	36.20
Africa	311	864	1266	9.44	12.35	13.04
Latin America (less temperate South America)	210	619	918	6.37	8.85	9.45
Other	3	10	15	0.13	0.14	0.16

[1] Includes Europe, USSR, Northern America, Japan, temperate South America, Australia, and New Zealand.
[2] Includes East Asia less Japan, South Asia, Africa, Latin America less temperate South America, and Oceania less Australia and New Zealand.
Source: Projections to 2000 are the United Nations' high variant. Estimates for 1965 are from the United Nations, *Demographic Yearbook 1966*, Table 1.

The world projections to 2018 produce a medium estimate of 9.7 billion, a high of 10.4 billion, and a low of 8.5 billion. In other words, these projections show the world's population increasing in the next half-century (from 1965 to 2018) by between 5.2 and 7.1 billion, with the medium rise 6.4 billion. Using the assumptions about the decrease in fertility in the developing regions implicit in the U.N. high projections to 2000 and in its medium projections from 2000 to 2018, world population will still nearly triple in the next half-century. Even the lowest of the projections regarded as reasonable would in the next fifty years produce more than a doubling (an increase of 157 percent), while the highest will produce more than a tripling (an increase of 215 percent).

The magnitude of the anticipated population growth can be seen by comparing actual growth during the first half of this century with the anticipated growth during the second half and to the year 2018. Between 1900 and 1950, world population increased by less than a billion. Between 1950 and 2000, under the U.N. high projection (which allows for some fertility decline), it will increase by some 4.5 billion. For the period 2000 to 2018, under this writer's medium projection, it will increase by an additional 2.7 billion. Thus, during the first half of the 20th century, world population increased by an average of 20 million per year; during the second half, it could increase by an average of 90 million per year; during the first eighteen years of the 21st century, it could increase by an average of about 150 million per year. The latter figure represents an increment to world population every 15 months that equals the present population of the United States (some 200 million).

By 2018, the less developed areas could have a medium population of 7.7 billion, the developed areas a medium of 2 billion. The population of the less developed areas during the next half-century would thus increase by 5.5 billion, or by three and a half times. In contrast, the developed areas would not quite double, with an increment of less than a billion (942 million). By 2018, under these projections, the less developed areas will embrace 79.6 percent of the world's people, compared to 68.5 percent in 1965 and 77.5 percent in 2000.

In the next half-century, under these projections, Asia will increase its proportion of the world's population from about 53 to 57 percent, with South Asia rising from 30 to 36 percent and East Asia declining from 23 to 21 percent. It should be emphasized that these figures do little more than show general magnitude and perhaps give some sense of relative standing; the estimates for East Asia are especially speculative.

Latin America, in the next fifty years, will show the greatest relative increase, growing from 6.3 to 9.5 percent of the world's total, a proportionate gain of more than 50 percent; Africa would have a proportionate gain of over a third, rising from 9.4 to 13 percent of the world's total.

Among the more developed areas, Europe (excluding the U.S.S.R.) will experience the greatest relative decline, shrinking from 13.5 to 6.8 percent of the world's population, a relative loss of about 50 percent; North America will decline from 6.5 to 5.1 percent, a proportionate decline of over a third; and the Soviet Union will drop by more than a fifth, from 7 to 5.5 percent.

How Can We Feed All These People?

No matter which of these projections is accepted, the implications for present and prospective population growth remain essentially the same.[3] In the long run, such growth rates cannot possibly persist, because the finite dimensions of this planet set a limit to the population it can sustain. In the short run, crucial problems that are bound to generate crisis situations are manifest in the economic and political consequences of the anticipated population increases. Involved are significant implications for levels of living and world politics.

Let us examine first the often discussed relation of population growth to resources, and especially to food supply. A recent analysis of the world resources picture by Joseph L. Fisher and Neal Potter of Resources for the Future, Inc.,[4] indicates that there is justification neither for the belief that the world is faced with the imminent exhaustion of critical materials nor for the belief that man's ingenuity can solve all the problems posed by the increasing pressure of population upon resources. Rather, the picture on raw materials is mixed. The world outlook, and that for the developing areas in general, is fairly good in respect to energy commodities, especially when one reckons on the potential of the energy of the atom. But for food the prospect is less favorable, and in the past several years it has turned dismal.

Almost a doubling of world food output is needed now to supply a nutritionally adequate diet to the present populations in the less developed areas. If an adequate diet is to be achieved for a world population that will be more than double by 2000, food production must more than quadruple by the end of the century. This will require greater annual increases in food production than have ever been attained over a prolonged period of time. Moreover, within the past few years population growth has outdistanced food production in many areas. A study completed by Lester R. Brown of the U.S. Department of Agriculture in 1965 indicates that in Asia food per person had declined by 4 percent since 1961, and in Latin America by 6 percent. In Africa, food production had so far kept up with population increase, but a decline in per capita food production seemed imminent.[5]

The Food and Agriculture Organization Report of October, 1966, stated: "World food production failed to rise in 1965-1966, but population increased by about 70 million persons. . . . Per person production of food fell by about 2 percent [for the world]. Per capita production dropped by 4 to 5 percent in the developing regions of Africa, Latin America, and the Far East."

Thus the evidence is that the increase in food production after World War II (during the war production greatly declined) leveled off around 1960 and since then has failed to keep pace with population growth. The prospect of food shortages in Asia, parts of Latin America, and Africa within the next decade or so cannot be easily dismissed.[6]

Critical problems face the world during the next half-century, however, even if the threat of lower levels of living or mass starvation fails to materialize, i.e., even if present levels of living are maintained in the less developed areas. A failure to achieve substantially higher levels of living consonant with the rising expectations of the mass populations of the world, and with the national aspirations of the postwar nations, is likely to result in explosive situations threatening world peace.

The role of population in determining the world's economic and political destinies during the next half-century may be grasped by considering simultaneously the following propositions:

1. We live in a world of have and have-not nations.

2. Differences among nations in levels of living, by reason of the "revolution of rising expectations," have become "felt" differences.

3. The have-not nations are striving to achieve higher living levels and they have made this goal (apart from independence, for those that have not yet achieved it) their major national aspiration.

4. There is an inverse correlation between levels of living and present or projected rates of population growth.

5. Rapid population growth is obstructing efforts to raise levels of living in the developing regions of the world.

6. Despite national and international efforts to raise levels of living, disparities between have and have-not nations are increasing rather than decreasing.

7. The accelerating rate of urbanization in the developing areas is exacerbating social unrest, political instability, and threats to world peace.

8. The bipolar world political alignment — the confrontation between capitalist and communist nations, or the East-West cold war — is augmenting the tensions arising from frustrations in efforts to raise levels of living in the developing regions.

9. The bipolar political world is being fragmented by a have and have-not division within the communist bloc and by the Gaullist schism in the West. A possible world political realignment may occur on a have and have-not basis rather than on the present capitalist-communist basis. This would produce a North-South rather than an East-West confrontation.

Each of these propositions has been fully elaborated on elsewhere.[7] Here it must suffice to say that the population prospect over the next half-century is one of the factors that make the world economic and political outlook an unhappy one. A world population of 9.7 billion by 2018 means that the increment alone in the next fifty years would be twice the present world population (which took 2 to 2.5 million years to evolve). Such growth is bound to impede efforts to increase levels of living in the developing nations in Asia, Africa, and Latin America.

Realism compels us to recognize that to change the world population and economic outlook substantially requires a major reallocation of present world resources in combination with a program of economic development and population control. Such a prospect is not yet in sight. Moreover, even if funds of sufficient magnitude were available, it is by no means certain that we possess, as yet, the knowledge to expend those monies to adequate effect. In consequence, it may be expected that the next fifty years will be characterized by increased, not decreased, social unrest; greater, not lesser, political instabilities; intensified, not diminished, cold war between capitalist and communist blocs and between have and have-not nations; more, not fewer, threats to world peace;

greater, not smaller, military expenditures; higher, not lower, taxes; and larger, not smaller, government in the United States.

Given the present outlook, only the faithful who believe in miracles from heaven, the optimistic who anticipate superwonders from science, the parochial fortunate who think they can continue to exist on islands of affluence in a sea of world poverty, and the naive who anticipate nothing can look to the future with equanimity.

U.S. Foreign Policy and Birth Control

Until recently, the United States has had implicit rather than explicit population policies on both the international and domestic fronts. Cumulative and accelerating developments have, however, forced the government into more direct confrontation with the problem. But, since policy is still being formulated and action programs are barely under way, it is important to consider the issues involved.

First of all, it should be noted that consensus has been virtually achieved, internationally and within the U.S., on the need to dampen rates of world population growth. This can be achieved in only two ways: by increasing the death rate (or refusing to lower it), or by decreasing the birth rate. The adoption of a policy to increase the death rate is universally untenable. Only one way remains, then, to decelerate rates of population growth — fertility control.

There is ground for encouragement in the fact that major organized opposition to fertility control, namely, in the Roman Catholic Church and in the communist world, has significantly diminished. But a number of issues remain to be resolved.

There is, for one thing, the argument that to increase standards of living the emphasis must be placed on economic development rather than on population control. It has been pointed out, and appropriately so, that fertility control alone does not necessarily increase income per capita.

The answer to this argument lies in recognition of the fact that *population growth must be controlled and productivity increased simultaneously.* Population control is no substitute for investment in capital goods and human resources, nor for achieving production know-how and entrepreneurship. It may, however, facilitate and increase the effectiveness of more direct efforts to achieve economic advances. The fact that fertility control alone will not necessarily produce higher standards of living must not be taken as grounds for neglecting it as an element in a program of economic development.

The second argument, of which Colin Clark, the noted economist, is perhaps the outstanding exponent, is that fertility control might retard rather than promote economic advances because it would diminish incentive. This thesis holds that the increasing misery caused by growing population pressures on land and other resources provides the motivation for man to improve his lot. To the extent that diminished population growth removes this pressure and the incentive for advancement it creates, standards of living would worsen rather than improve. To anyone who has lived in, or visited, the less developed areas of Asia, Latin America, or Africa, this argument is immediately seen to be defective. It is simply unrealistic, if not blind, to hold that, for example, what India needs to generate the motivation for advance is still more misery.

A third argument against the need for population control in order to achieve economic development flows from the socialist and communist thesis that world poverty is largely the result of the maldistribution of the world's production. While a more equitable distribution would undoubtedly raise the living level of the have-not peoples, it is not difficult to demonstrate that it would also tend to bring universal poverty rather than universal affluence. In 1962, the world average product per capita was $489. This was 17 percent of per capita product in North America and about half of per capita product in Europe. Total world production of goods and services in 1962 could therefore supply only 1.5 billion at the European level of living and only 500 million at the North American level, as compared with the actual world population of over 3 billion. Thus, by these criteria, it would seem either that the world was overpopulated by some 1.5 billion to 2.5 billion or that world production was far too low to eliminate poverty. In either case, it is clear that the achievement of a high world standard of living requires vast increases in world productivity and production rather than a mere redistribution of the world's product.

A fourth point of disagreement on the need for fertility control is the present contention of the Soviet Union that birth rates will come down automatically with increased industrialization and urbanization. This argument has some basis, in the sense that there are no examples of peoples who have achieved high levels of industrialization and urbanization, and with them literacy and higher levels of living, among whom the birth rate has not fallen. But it is also true that there has usually been a considerable lag between reaching a relatively high level of industrialization and urbanization and the lowering of the birth rate.

The industrial nations achieved their economic development and low birth rates while their populations were relatively sparse in relation to land and other resources. In many of the less developed nations, and especially those containing the bulk of the world's population, population densities are already so great as to retard economic development. Moreover, even if the underdeveloped nations succeed in achieving industrialization at their present population growth rates, they will be far less able than were the advanced nations to pay the high price demanded by the great lag between industrialization and lowered birth rates. It is, therefore, unreasonable to oppose positive efforts to reduce rates of population growth by means of fertility control programs.

By reason, then, of the relation of population growth to economic development and world politics, and of the gains to be achieved through fertility control, the recently adopted U.S. policy of recognizing the need for reducing growth rates in the world as a whole, and especially in the less developed areas, is sound. We are openly, and on an ever larger scale, providing birth control knowledge, devices, and financial aid to the developing countries that request such aid and are simultaneously promoting more effective population control domestically for groups that have hitherto not adopted family planning practices. Aside from other considerations, the domestic program is important to negate the accusation that U.S. advocacy of population control abroad is a new form of imperialism.

While the U.S. must of necessity consider population as an element in any program of foreign economic aid, it should not attempt to enforce adoption of birth control measures as a condition for aid. Where it is clear that excessive population growth is obstructing economic development, we would, of course, be less than astute not to direct the attention of the developing nation to this fact, and, over the long run, we should be prepared to discontinue aid altogether whenever population or other factors clearly render it ineffective. But the decision on population control must be the aid recipient's.

How effective have birth control programs been to date, and how can they be improved? Progress in the developed areas may be termed adequate, but this is not true of the less developed nations. While death rates in Asia, Latin America, and Africa are declining much more rapidly than they ever did in economically advanced areas, their birth rates, as has been indicated, are still at traditionally high levels. Some decreases in birth rates are evident in localities that are experiencing rapid economic and social change, such as Taiwan, Hong Kong, Singapore, and South Korea, but the exceptions are few and involve only a small fraction of the two-thirds of the world population embraced by the developing areas.

It is not at all clear that the problem can be solved during the remainder of this century. The results of experiments to induce birth control among illiterate and poor populations have been disheartening. They indicate that such nations as India and China cannot be expected to greatly reduce their birth rates in the near future.

The picture does have its encouraging side, however. Never before have so many nations adopted family planning programs as a matter of national policy. Never before has so much been done in the fields of biomedicine and the social sciences in the hunt for better methods of fertility control. And never before has the prospect been so good that the United States will, as it should, use its fabulous resources to support the necessary research.

The question remains as to whether world population control is possible. For the economically advanced areas, the answer appears to be "yes," for they need do only a little more of what they are already doing. For the developing nations, which by 2018 may have four-fifths of the world's population, the answer is, "We do not know." But there is one thing we do know. We cannot afford not to exert every effort to help the developing nations control their birth rates. Fortunately, this has now become the policy not only of the United States, but also of the United Nations and the World Health Organization.

NOTES

1. United Nations, *World Population Prospects,* United Nations, New York, 1966.
2. In view of the attention they have received, mention should also be made of the projections by Donald J. Bogue, based on the assumption that "the prospects for rapid fertility control are excellent . . ." and that "population trends before 1960 are largely irrelevant in predicting what will happen in the future. . . ." Bogue presents as his estimate of world population in 2000 the number 4.5 billion (in "The End of the Population Explosion," *The Public Interest,* No. 7, Spring, 1967, pp. 12ff). This number is regarded by the present writer, as indicated elsewhere, as too unrealistic to warrant further attention. See Philip M. Hauser, "Family Planning and Population Programs: A Book Review Article," *Demography,* Vol. IV, No. 1, 1967, pp. 397-414.

3. This section is based largely on Philip M. Hauser, *World Population Problems,* Headline Series, Foreign Policy Association, No. 174, December, 1965, pp. 15ff.
4. Joseph L. Fisher and Neal Potter, "Resources in the United States and the World," in Philip M. Hauser, ed., *The Population Dilemma,* The American Assembly, Columbia University, Prentice Hall, Inc., Englewood Cliffs, New Jersey, 1963, pp. 94ff.
5. Lester R. Brown, *Increasing World Food Output: Problems and Prospects,* Washington, D.C., U.S. Department of Agriculture, Economic Research Service, 1965.
6. Raymond Ewell, "Losing Battle to Feed the Hungry," *U.S. Department of State News Letter,* January, 1967.
7. Philip M. Hauser, *op. cit.,* pp. 15ff.

CHAPTER 12

ECONOMICS

The Rich Will Grow Richer and the Poor Comparatively Poorer

by Herman Kahn and Anthony J. Wiener

A problem of long-range speculation is that one particular course of events may seem no more likely than a number of others. In order to avoid the dilemma of Buridan's ass, who starved midway between two bales of hay because he could not decide which he preferred, we must make arbitrary choices among almost equally plausible possibilities. Clearly the most salient of these possibilities is a projection that is "surprise-free," one that assumes the continuation of trends now apparent while excluding dramatic and surprising events of the sort that overtook the major nations of the world in the first two-thirds of this century.

Herman Kahn is cofounder and director of the Hudson Institute at Harmon-on-Hudson, N.Y. For more than ten years before that, he was a defense analyst with the RAND Corporation. He is the author of On Thermonuclear War *and* Thinking About the Unthinkable.

Anthony J. Wiener, a lawyer and social scientist, is chairman of the Research Management Council at the Hudson Institute. He has also been associated with the consulting firm of Arthur D. Little, Inc., and the Massachusetts Institute of Technology.

Adapted from The Year 2000 *by Herman Kahn and Anthony J. Wiener, published by The Macmillan Company, New York. Copyright © 1967 by the Hudson Institute, Inc. Adapted by permission of the authors and the publisher.*

Thus the crucial assumption of this study is that present economic trends will continue more or less smoothly through the year 2000 and perhaps beyond, uninterrupted by world wars, world depressions, or other cataclysms. This seems to us quite plausible, despite much anxiety about thermonuclear war, and about the war in Vietnam, or, indeed, despite much anxiety about many issues, especially regarding relations between the developed and the underdeveloped nations and the possibility of famine in the latter. In the face of these anxieties, we nevertheless sense a growing consensus that the world is entering a period of general political and economic stability, particularly with regard to the frontiers and economies of the older nations.

In addition to the modest East-West détente already achieved, there is a better understanding on both sides of the Iron Curtain of the motives, objectives, and style of the opponent (colored slightly, perhaps, by some wishful thinking). Communism has had a relative lack of success in Africa and Latin America, and even in South and Southeast Asia. A number of technical developments and changes in strategic forces and doctrine seem to have mitigated many important aspects of the arms race and reduced the possibilities of either premeditated or accidental war. Most of all, political passion and ideological commitment appear to have ebbed in the major nations, making people simply unwilling to risk war over the issues in international conflict.

A new factor tending toward stability is the relative lack of pressure for territorial expansion. While boundary disputes, irredentism, and territorial aggrandizement may continue, as they have throughout history, to create instabilities for some of the new nations, the general assessment is that, for most of the older countries, frontier questions are no longer dominating or even serious. (A possible exception, of course, is Germany, and we should also admit the possibility of Chinese territorial aggression.)

Another significant development is the formation of "pluralistic security communities" (on the model of U.S.-Canadian relations), which are based on the assumption that war (or violent change) is unthinkable. This type of community is an important step toward political integration or unification. Western Europe is the most notable example, but the trend is evident in Latin America, too. Before 1940, most experts judged Latin American relations to be unstable and the probability of war high. Now, few would be surprised if the Latin American map of 2018 did not look much the same as today, with the possible exception of some transnational communities — economic and possibly political — which do not erase the old national frontiers. Most of the old and many of the new nations today enjoy a high degree of security on their frontiers and the benefits of access to world trade with little, if any, explicit need for a national military capability to enforce their rights and privileges. This situation probably will continue.

If these conjectures prove accurate, there is reason to believe that the sustained economic growth of the post-World War II era will be maintained. This raises the real possibility of worldwide industrialization and the emergence in more advanced nations of what might be called a post-industrial culture. Some of the economic growth clearly derives from a growing sophistication in governmental economic policies. It is widely believed that — with the possible exception of China — almost all the communist and capitalist governments alike are coming to understand better how to keep their economies stable and growing. We believe that current government success in economics and planning is a major cause of the emergence of mass consumption societies in Western Europe, the U.S., Japan, and Australia, and is one reason why such societies can be expected to emerge rapidly in the Soviet Union and Eastern Europe.

An Optimistic Bias

Assuming continued progress in the development of new technologies and in government planning, we postulate that the current rates of such factors as increases in productivity will be equalled or bettered over the long run in the next fifty years. We shall now proceed to write a moderately optimistic economic "scenario" of how things may go, barring major wars and depressions, for the next half-century.

What we mean by optimistic is illustrated in the accompanying graph,[1] which projects the per capita gross national product (GNP) of the U.S. In the graph, "m" is the *medium forecast* derived from the steepest possible *long-term* trend through 1959 and 1966, while "M" (our preferred projection) is the medium typically in line with recent *short-term* trends but exceeding the long-term trend and projected as a straight line from 1882-86 through 1966. "H" and "L" represent the extremes that can reasonably be extrapolated from the available data.

The accompanying table applies this contrast in GNP projections to ten major countries. The "medium" forecast, which we prefer, is the medium projection based on recent short-term trends.

U.S. GROSS NATIONAL PRODUCT PER CAPITA, 1869-2000 (1965 DOLLARS)

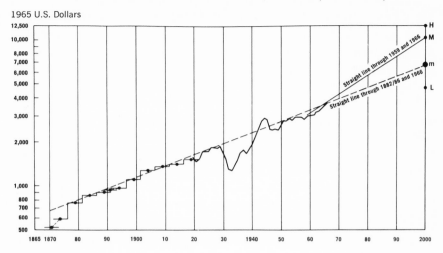

Comparative Forecasts of GNP Per Capita to Year 2000 for Ten Major Countries

	1965 GNP/CAP.	Medium Forecast		Forecast Using More Long-Term Trend		Earliest Data for Long-Term Trend
		Growth Rate	Year 2000 GNP/CAP.	Growth Rate	Year 2000 GNP/CAP.	
	1965 U.S. $	% Per Year	1965 U.S. $	% Per Year	1965 U.S. $	
U.S.	3557	3.0	10160	1.8	6750	1869-73
Canada	2464	3.1	7070	1.6	4300	1870-79
France	1964	3.7	6830	1.6	3400	1810-20
W. Germany	1905	4.1	7790	1.8	3600	1860-69
U.K.	1804	3.7	6530	1.5	3000	1860-69
U.S.S.R.	1288	3.7	4650	2.8	3400	1870
Italy	1101	4.1	4450	2.4	2500	1862-68
Japan	857	6.8	8590	3.7	3100	1878-87
India	99	2.9	270	2.1	205	1950
China	98	3.5	321	3.1	285	1933
Unweighted average		4.1		2.3		

In general, our preference for the more optimistic projection derives from the increased rate at which new technology is being developed, applied, and diffused, from the institutionalization of a policy of growth by governments around the world, and from anticipated increases in world productivity. We believe these factors are likely to outweigh other important considerations that point away from an increase in the rate of long-term growth in per capita income.

The U.S. and U.S.S.R. Will Still Be the Only Superpowers

Power and influence in international relations are multidimensional concepts that include, among other things, military capabilities, size, wealth, geographic position, and such less precise notions as stature, prestige, and culture. In order to make projections that incorporate some quantitative measurement of these characteristics, we use three simple indices: population, gross national product, and per capita GNP. The first two are proxies for size, and all three are indications of the potential for political importance.

As indicated, our projections have been extrapolated from current data and recent experience, with modifications where recent experience seems unlikely to continue. If we took the projections too seriously — either by taking the indices as the *sine qua non* of power or by regarding the "surprise-free" estimates as something more than a scenario — we would be subject to valid criticism. Per capita GNP is a poor measure of per capita surplus over and above subsistence, since, for one thing, the subsistence level probably rises along with income. And even if GNP, population, and GNP per capita were perfect indices of power in international affairs, estimates of them are notoriously unreliable and GNP's have many non-comparable aspects.

But, despite all the arguments that can be raised against the use of these three indices, it is difficult to find examples among the nations considered important in today's world that do not rank high on at least one of these scales, and it is equally difficult to find the opposite case. In any event, one must ask: What other measures of national power would do as well? Would they be any more reliable? Could they be any more accurately projected into the future?

Using our three indices, then, we suggest that the international hierarchy of 2018 is likely to show ten major powers, with the U.S. and the U.S.S.R. still the superpowers. Japan, West Germany, France, China, and the United Kingdom are likely to be considered large powers; India, Italy, and Canada, intermediate powers. The next 120 nations can be thought of as small powers. The ranking is generally a simple one of estimated GNP for the middle and late 1970's. The intermediate powers have at least half again the GNP of the small powers, the large powers have one-third again the GNP of the intermediate, and the superpowers have more than twice the GNP of the large powers.

It should be noted that this ordering will seem reasonable by other criteria than gross national product. An assessment of relative potential military power and influence on a large range of issues in a large range of situations, for example, is likely to produce much the same ordering, although with some sharp changes for specific issues and some sharp changes for specific situations.

Relationship of GNP and Population

Estimates of real per capita GNP for the ten major countries and (as shown later) the nineteen "contender" countries were made by extrapolating a fraction of which the numerator constituted projected GNP and the denominator projected population. The consequent per capita GNP is thus the arithmetic result of two independently extrapolated variables.

This method seems to imply that aggregate economic activity, the rate of growth of output, and population growth are independent factors. It is clear, however, that they cannot so neatly be divorced from one another, although their precise interrelationship is less clear, especially with respect to the less developed countries (LDC's). For example, cogent arguments can be presented both pro and con the advisability of a large population at a given point in time. More appropriate is the issue of the rate of population growth and its effect on economic development. The majority view (at least with respect to LDC's) is that rapid population growth impedes economic development. Age distribution is a significant factor here. A continued high birth rate produces a substantial ratio of young dependents, which implies increased national expenditures for consumption and on such factors as health and education, with a consequent reduction in savings and in funds available for industrial development. Another issue faced by LDC's is the "population trap," wherein gains in per capita income tend to be accompanied by new public health activities that lower mortality rates, with the result that the population increases and the per capita gain is erased.

The evidence in the accompanying table concerning population and per capita growth in income is not conclusive, but it does show that, out of thirty-seven LDC's, only three have failed to show gains in real per capita income during a recent period.

Comparison of Population Growth Rates with Per Capita Income Growth Rates in 37 Less Developed Countries

Rate of Population Growth (Percent Per Year)	Rate of Growth of Real Per Capita Income (Percent Per Year)						
	Total	Less Than Zero	0 to 0.9	1.0 to 1.9	2.0 to 2.9	3.0 to 3.9	4.0 to 4.9	5.0 And Over
Total	37	3	4	12	12	2	2	2
3.5 and over	2	1	0	0	0	0	1	0
3.0-3.4	10	0	2	3	4	0	1	0
2.5-2.9	11	1	2	5	1	1	0	1
2.0-2.4	8	0	0	3	5	0	0	0
1.5-1.9	4	1	0	0	2	1	0	0
Less than 1.5	2	0	0	1	0	0	0	1

This table shows the frequency distribution of developing nations by growth rate of real per capita income cross-classified by growth rate of population, 1957-58 to 1963-64. The countries included are non-communist ones in Africa, Asia, and Latin America (omitting Israel, Japan, and the Republic of South Africa) with populations of around 2 million or more, for which data were available.

Thus, at the risk of oversimplification, we have projected product and population independently in our estimates. In general, high GNP extrapolations were associated with high population estimates, both for LDC's and for developed countries, and low with low. However, in the case of China and India, the low GNP estimate was associated with high population in the computation of per capita product and vice versa. This adjustment makes explicit the conclusion that, in these two countries, the existence of a large population will work to reduce the level of aggregate product.

We must emphasize again that this procedure of projection should be taken with several grains of salt. The indices chosen are mechanical and do not adequately reflect the subtleties of national affluence, power, quality of life, and other consequences one might wish to infer from them. The growth rates are somewhat arbitrary and projections based on them can easily be wrong. The projections indicate only what would happen if all the assumptions, including those on growth rates, proved true. While this is an interesting possibility, it is still an unlikely one; its merit is that all other specific possibilities seem still more unlikely.

This warning having been delivered, we now project the world to the year 2000. We see a population of 6.4 billion, slightly more than twice the 1965 population of 3.3 billion. Africa and South America show the greatest population growth rates, both 2.7 percent, but 58 percent of the world's peoples remain Asian. Gross world product will rise from $2.1 trillion in 1965 to $10.9 trillion (1965 U.S. dollars), the consequence of the relatively high growth rates we have assumed, averaging 4.8 percent annually. Reducing the rate to 3 percent will bring gross world product in 2000 to $6 trillion, only 55 percent of the figure based on the 4.8 percent rate.

In 1965, per capita world product was about $630, approximately one-sixth of the U.S. figure. By the year 2000, per capita world product could be $1,700, within a range of $880 to $2,200, depending on the growth rates projected for individual countries. Per capita product could thus increase over 1965 by one-half or by almost four times, given the normal high and low within which we are working. The distribution of world product by continent is projected to shift in favor of the developing countries, with the relative shares of Europe and North America reduced by 6 percent below 1965. This is partly due to the growing importance of Japan, which, by virtue of its location only, is included in the "developing" continent of Asia.

Again, mainly because of the impressive growth of Japan's economy coupled with its low population growth, Asia is projected to achieve the highest rates of growth in GNP and per capita GNP. Africa's GNP growth of 4.6 percent, although high, will be offset by substantial population expansion. South America is also anticipated to sustain considerable population growth, and this will limit that continent's per capita GNP growth. See the accompanying table of growth rates for each continent.

Average Annual Rates of Growth of Population, Gross National Product, and Per Capita GNP, by Continent, 1965-2000

	Population	GNP	Per Capita GNP
Africa	2.7	4.6	2.0
Asia	1.9	5.9	3.9
Europe	0.8	4.6	3.8
Oceania	1.7	3.9	2.2
North America	1.9	4.5	2.5
South America	2.7	4.6	1.9
World	1.8	4.8	2.9

Turning now to the performance of the ten major countries, it is to be noted that the medium forecast for per capita GNP in the year 2000 shows some interesting changes from the 1965 ranking. While the U.S. maintains its top position, Japan moves into second place from its 1965 position of eighth and West Germany climbs to third over Canada and France. If the per capita GNP projection is extended to the year 2020, the medium forecast is for changes at both the top and bottom of the ranking. Japan takes the lead from the U.S. by a large margin, $33,200 to $18,600, while China, with $681, climbs to ninth place, displacing India, with $552.

World population in the twenty years ending in 2020 is assumed to grow at about the same rate as in 1965-2000, to reach nine billion. Over half will live in Asia; only one-fifth will live in Europe and North America, as compared with the present three-tenths. In the same period, gross world product will rise 5 percent a year. Asia's share will reach one-fourth of the total, as compared with the present one-eighth, largely because of the 7.5 percent GNP growth rate assumed for Japan. Per capita world output in 2020 will be approximately five times the 1965 figure.

Disparity Among Nations

Obviously, the per capita world GNP growth rate is a composite of the disparate rates of individual nations. (We have assumed that foreign aid programs, tariff agreements, trade patterns, international economic institutions, and the like will continue much as they are.) The disparity can be shown most simply by contrasting the economic performances of the industrially developed and the less developed countries. The widening gap between the developed and less developed nations, shown in the accompanying tables, would be further heightened by putting such countries as Albania, Portugal, Mexico, and other Central American republics in the "less developed world" and by placing Venezuela, Argentina, Israel, the Republic of South Africa, and a few others in the "developed world."

In 1965 the less developed world, as defined as follows, contained about 68 percent of the world's population but produced only 14.5 percent of its output. By the year 2000, it will have three-quarters of the world population but will produce no more proportionately than it did in 1965. However, since its growth in output will exceed its population growth,

The Widening Gap Between the Developed
and Less Developed Nations

GNP in Billions of 1965 U.S. Dollars

Less Developed World

	1965	2000
Africa	43.9	216.0
Asia less Japan	203.4	1,081.0
South America	59.4	292.0
Total	306.7	1,589.0

Developed World

	1965	2000
Japan	84.0	1,056.0
North America	774.2	3,620.0
Oceania	28.0	107.0
Europe	923.9	4,476.0
Total	1,810.1	9,259.0
World Total	2,116.8	10,848.0

Per Capita GNP in 1965 U.S. Dollars

	1965	2000
Less Developed World	135	325
Developed World	1,675	5,775
World Total	631	1,696

there will be an increase in per capita GNP amounting to a real growth of some 2.8 percent over the period 1965-2000. The industrialized continents plus Japan will perform remarkably better, implying an annual growth of about 3.6 percent in per capita GNP.

Thus, while in 1965 the per capita product of the developed world was about twelve times that of the less developed world, by 2000 it will be nearly eighteen times greater — a 50 percent increase in the gap. Whether the peoples of the LDC's find satisfaction in their absolute progress or dissatisfaction in the increasing discrepancy between rich and poor depends on many economic, political, and cultural factors.

Another and rather startling view of the gap as it already exists is shown in the following table that indicates how many years it will take various countries to reach the U.S. 1965 per capita GNP of $3,557. This table projects that by 2018 only 15 nations will have achieved the *present* U.S. level of GNP per capita.

Years Needed to Achieve Current U.S. GNP Per Capita

	1965 GNP Per Capita (1965 U.S. $)	Number of Years Needed to Reach $3,600 Per Capita*
Sweden	$2497	11
Canada	2464	12
West Germany	1905	16
East Germany	1574	17
France	1924	18
United Kingdom	1804	19
Czechoslovakia	1554	20
Japan	857	22
Israel	1334	24
Australia	2009	25
U.S.S.R.	1288	28
Italy	1101	30
Poland	962	34
Romania	757	38
New Zealand	1932	42
Argentina	492	69
Taiwan	221	71
U.A.R.	166	97
Thailand	126	98
China	98	101
S. Africa and S. W. Africa	503	115
India	99	117
Brazil	280	130
Pakistan	91	144
Mexico	455	162
Nigeria	83	339
Colombia	277	358
Indonesia	99	593

* The number of years needed to reach $3,600 per capita was calculated on the basis of the 1965 GNP for each country and the "medium" rate we projected for growth of population and GNP.

To round out the world projections, we present an accompanying table of the expected economic performances of 19 "contending" countries — countries that because of their present or potential economic power rank just below the majors. It should be noted that of these Sweden has the highest per capita GNP in 2000, as it does now, exceeding also all the ten major countries except the United States. In this projection Australia and New Zealand drop from their 1965 second and third places to fifth and sixth, yielding to East Germany and Czechoslovakia. Among the less developed countries, Argentina and Taiwan do well.

Nineteen Contender Countries' GNP Per Capita
(Medium Estimates in 1965 U.S. Dollars)

	1965	1975	1985	2000
Sweden	2,497	3,535	5,078	8,679
Australia	2,009	2,568	3,218	4,612
New Zealand	1,932	2,250	2,544	3,195
East Germany (including E. Berlin)	1,574	2,529	4,065	8,355
Czechoslovakia	1,554	2,357	3,638	7,046
Israel	1,334	1,949	2,978	5,839
Poland	962	1,396	2,054	3,680
Romania	757	1,143	1,717	3,224
South Africa and Southwest Africa	503	598	699	906
Argentina	492	629	831	1,300
Mexico	455	503	558	680
Brazil	280	319	372	506
Colombia	277	298	322	359
Taiwan	221	314	456	837
U.A.R.	166	221	295	480
Thailand	126	170	239	402
Indonesia	99	107	112	123
Pakistan	91	109	134	200
Nigeria	83	94	107	125

In the U.S., 1 Family in 12 Will Live Like Millionaires

The U.S. labor force in 1967 stood at approximately 74 million persons employed in civilian pursuits. At an average of 2,000 hours of work per person annually, total man-hours totaled about 150 billion. With one man-hour yielding $5.20 of GNP, about $780 billion of GNP was achieved in 1967.

We believe that productivity will rise. Before World War II, the yearly increase in productivity per man-hour was a little over 2 percent; since the war, it has averaged about 3 percent, and a recent report by the Secretary of Labor indicates that new calculations give 3.8 percent as the average for the last five years. It is generally expected that the U.S. should average between 2.5 and 3.5 percent a year, at a minimum, over the next three to four decades, and some experts think that once automation hits its stride the increase will be another 1 or 2 percent higher. Given the optimistic bias of this scenario, 3 or 3.5 percent seems a likely figure on which to focus. We shall bound the reasonable possibilities of variation by low and high projections based on 2.5 and 4 percent.

Summary of United States Gross Economic Indices in 1965 U.S. Dollars

	1965	1975	1985	2000	2020
Population (in millions)	195	222	258	318	421
Households (in millions)	57.3	68.9	82.1	101.3	136.6
GNP (in billions)	$ 681				
Low		$ 918	$1,285	$ 2,177	$ 4,008
High		$1,062	$1,713	$ 3,628	$ 8,947
Per Capita GNP (in dollars)	$3,500				
Low		$4,150	$5,000	$ 6,850	$ 9,550
High		$4,800	$6,650	$11,550	$21,250
Index of Output per Man-Hour (1957-59 = 100)	126				
Low at 2.5 percent		160	205	296	389
High at 4 percent		185	274	494	867

Before World War II, a good part of the productivity increase was taken up by decreased hours of work and increased leisure time. Since the war, this trend has lessened. Today the average fully employed American works approximately 2,000 hours a year; if we extrapolate postwar trends, this should drop to somewhere between 1,700 and 1,900 hours a year by the year 2000. If, as seems probable, there is a renewed tendency to take up the increased productivity in increased leisure, the hours could conceivably drop substantially below 1,600 — possibly even below 1,000.

These, then, are our assumptions and the resulting high and low GNP forecasts for the United States to the year 2000:

For both forecasts:

Year 2000 population: 318 million

Percent employed: 38

Work year: 1,600 hours

For low GNP forecast ($2.2 trillion in 1965 dollars):

Productivity per man-hour rises 2.5 percent annually

For high GNP forecast ($3.6 trillion in 1965 dollars):

Productivity per man-hour rises 4 percent annually

The same high and low GNP's could be achieved, of course, by manipulating the three variables: percentage of population employed, annual hours worked per employed person, and annual rate of productivity increase. (In the calculation above, we chose 38 percent of population employed as the typical U.S. experience.) Permutations based on any reasonable handling of the variables lead to the conclusion that it would be surprising indeed if the U.S. failed to achieve the low GNP estimate, whereas the high estimate is barely within the "surprise-free" requirement.

Yet if productivity per man-hour increases around 3.5 percent a year, and if current work-oriented, achievement-oriented attitudes are maintained, it should be possible for the U.S. to reach the high projection, or even exceed it. In this high projection, we estimate that about one family in twelve would have an income after federal income tax of at least $50,000 a year. This is the level of income that we now associate with millionaires, and should be compared with the current ratio of only one family in several hundred with such an income.

By the year 2020 we expect the work year to drop to an average of 1,370 hours. Personal consumption expenditures are calculated to range from $2.7 trillion (1965 dollars) to $5.7 trillion, compared to $432 billion in 1965. Per capita consumption is projected to be between $6,400 and $13,600, compared to $2,200 in 1965. Thus the U.S. standard of living would rise from three to six times its 1965 level, accompanied by an increase in leisure time.

The accompanying table on the distribution of family income shows

Distribution of U.S. Family Personal Income Before Taxes* (1965 U.S. Dollars)

Income Class	Percent of Consumer Units† in Income Class				
	1965	1975	1985	2000	2020
Under $3,000	16.2	12.6	9.5	5.6	3.3
$3-6,000	26.2	19.6	12.9	7.0	3.8
$6-8,000	17.7	14.4	11.6	5.2	2.5
$8-10,000	12.7	13.8	11.3	6.6	3.0
$10-15,000	16.3	21.5	24.6	18.0	8.4
$15-25,000	7.9	13.2	20.3	30.4	31.4
$25-50,000	}	}	}	22.2	} 39.2
$50-100,000	} 3.0	} 4.9	} 9.8	}	} 15.1
	}	}	}	5.0	}
$100,000 and over	}	}	}	}	} 3.3
	100.0	100.0	100.0	100.0	100.0
Mean Family Personal Income	$8,380	$10,410	$13,380	$20,980	$34,920

* Before federal individual income tax.
† Families plus unrelated individuals.

roughly how the projected rise in national income will be distributed among American families. One should note that, by the year 2000, 27 percent of all families (or consumer units) will attain incomes of $25,000 or more before income taxes. And by 2020, about 58 percent of the families will have reached the $25,000 income level.

Unanswered Questions

Plausible or not, the "surprise-free" — or "standard" — world we have projected presents a useful subject for discussion and comparison, and, of course, it can accommodate many variations. Will the coming world tend to be more integrated, with a high degree of consultation among nations and perhaps increased political coordination? Will this world be *status quo* oriented or will it be, with respect to the less developed world, aid oriented? Or should we expect a more inward-looking world characterized by pluralism of power and political influence, a general preoccupation with national interests, and a low level of conflict? Will communism tend to erode or become more dynamic? Will there be a relative withdrawal from world affairs of the U.S. and the U.S.S.R. (as seems possible under certain circumstances), and their replacement by a dynamic Europe and/or Japan? Even without a major war, will we have a world in disarray, subject to constant tensions and small conflicts?

Any of these developments could have economic consequences that would considerably alter our projections. But let us optimistically assume a relatively prosperous, stable, increasingly integrated world that becomes more and more aid oriented. It is self-evident that a surprising amount of development can be achieved over a span of ten to thirty-five years if modest amounts of capital are made available by the developed countries (say, 1 to 3 percent of their GNP) and if this capital is efficiently absorbed by the LDC's. Assuming that it takes about $4 of capital to generate an income of $1 per capita, then $1 trillion of additional capital can increase the income of one billion people by an additional $250 per capita (above the $100-$300 otherwise to be expected). This means that by the year 2000 enough capital could be available to put most of the LDC's into the $500-plus per capita class, and all of them into the $300-$500 class. The earlier projections in this article assumed no such impressive progress by the LDC's.

A World Depression Could Happen

On the pessimistic side, but still within the context of our "standard world," there could develop an economic depression of major proportions, whose scenario might run as follows:

During the next decade, nations display an aimlessness in political affairs, solving none of their major problems. The Common Market becomes a restrictive customs union. The U.S. and the European Economic Community remain determined to protect agriculture to the detriment of West Germany, which intensifies its pursuit of East bloc markets. Beginning with the mid-1970's, U.S. unemployment steadily increases, the government maintains its deficit spending policies, and only leakage in the form of a continuing payments deficit prevents acute inflation. By the late 1970's, the world is saturated with dollars. The developing countries are converting their gains to gold, and the U.S. gold supply is diminishing rapidly. In the U.S., the political consensus of the '50's and '60's erodes, and public opinion is polarized around the radical right and the protesting left. The President finds himself the hapless heir to international overcommitment and domestic inflation and the leader of a shrinking middle ground. With a political campaign a year away, there is agreement on only one point of domestic policy: there should be no tax increase.

At this point, bickering between West Germany and the other EEC members becomes openly vehement, and Bonn concludes sweeping treaties with the East bloc and defiantly devalues the mark. In the traditional spirit of *noblesse oblige* toward Europe, the President turns to the Board of Governors of the International Monetary Fund instead of attempting to meet the crisis unilaterally. This proves to be a tragic mistake. The rest of the world concludes that the meeting is a prelude to devaluation, and a run on the dollar begins. The President, left with no other choice, makes the dollar inconvertible, and the pound sterling follows. Panic ensues, and, although it is short-lived in the developed countries, no nation or constellation of nations exists with the power to restore order to the international economic system.

Worldwide depression leads to social and political unrest; governments fall; people go hungry; state socialism gets a new lease on life. The straight, upward-inclining lines of our "standard world" projections are set back by several decades.

The Uncertainty of the Future

Not only is it difficult to make projections forward from the present; it is equally difficult to draw helpful inferences for the present from future possibilities. Yet clearly it is desirable to have some concept of where future policies may lead before the policies are formulated, lest the point of no return be passed before there is any conscious awareness that the panoply of choices is so great and the future so uncertain.

Only limited aspects of our projections are based entirely on technological extrapolations. "Wild" speculation is also needed to provide an imaginative perspective within which alternate choices can acquire a deeper, if not necessarily more exact, meaning. They are heuristic methods for studying the future, a future that will be upon us sooner than we like to believe. Although it is all of fifty years to the year 2018, it is already twenty-three years since the conclusion of World War II — an event that changed the lives of many of us. If we are as intellectually unprepared for events at the beginning of the 21st century, and as much lacking in understanding of the issues as we were in 1929, 1941, and 1947, we are likely to be in for some unpleasant surprises. More than that, we are likely to unnecessarily exacerbate and prolong the negative consequences of those surprises — perhaps to the extent that desirable institutions and values will be irrevocably overwhelmed.

NOTES

1. All tables and graphs in this article are drawn from *The Year 2000,* Herman Kahn and Anthony J. Wiener, Macmillan, New York, 1967, pp. 118-184.

CHAPTER 13

OCEANOGRAPHY

Man Will Turn Increasingly to the Sea for Resources, Recreation —and Possibly War

by Roger Revelle

What will we be doing in the ocean fifty years from now? One answer is simple: Everything we are doing today. We will fish, swim, and dive in it, sail on it, pollute it, study and measure it, use it for defense and military operations, drill and mine it for petroleum, natural gas, and minerals, obtain fresh water and other chemicals from solution, farm it, and use it as a pasture for protein production.

The major difference in these activities will be that some of them will be conducted on a far larger scale than today. Much of the entire ocean will be used by man, and not simply, as at present, chiefly the inshore and coastal waters. But even in the 21st century the ocean areas near land will still be the principal scene of man's marine activities. This will be so because these are the regions where most of the fishes live, where most of the valuable fuel and mineral resources are concentrated, and where it is easiest for people to enjoy themselves in ocean recreation.

We will also do some things that are not possible or necessary now. We may be able to change the weather over and in the ocean. We may

Roger Revelle, an oceanographer, is Director of the Harvard Center for Population Studies. He is also Chairman of the U.S. National Committee for the International Biological Program.

want to live on it or in it. We may have to install an international system for detecting, identifying, and tracking missile-launching submarines, those most fearsome of all nuclear weapons-delivery systems. We may establish underwater national or international parks and marine wilderness areas. Possibly we will construct and use transoceanic pipelines to carry fossil fuels and other bulk cargoes.

Boundaries Will Be Pushed Seaward

The likely expansion of existing activities and the creation of new ones will require far-reaching changes in the law of the sea and the public order of the oceans. Perhaps they will lead to a powerful and multi-faceted international organization designed to ensure that all mankind can benefit from the sea's resources. The ancient doctrine of *res nullius* — that the resources of the sea are no man's property, and belong to him who captures them — is already being replaced by the concept of *res communis* — that marine resources are the common property of mankind, and should be managed and used in the interests of all.

Around every continent there is a submerged, shallow plain, formed by waves during the Ice Age, when a part of the ocean waters was locked up in the continental glaciers and the sea level was several hundred feet lower than at present. This "continental shelf" varies greatly in width, from a mile or so off Chile and Peru to several hundred miles off East and Southeast Asia. On it lie reefs of phosphatic rock, and fossil beaches with placer deposits of tin, diamonds, thorium, and magnetic iron. Beneath it are ancient marine sediments that contain enormous quantities of petroleum, natural gas, sulfur, and salt.

. Beyond the shelf the continental platforms extend outward toward the deep sea, gradually deepening down to a mile or more. Like the shelf itself, this "continental slope" is underlain by sedimentary rock, and in many places it may also contain pools of oil, natural gas, and sulfur. Indeed, it has been estimated that as much as half of all the petroleum still remaining in the earth exists in the parts of the continents that lie beneath the ocean, even though these areas are less than a third the size of the dry land areas. The underwater reserves are probably at least 10 billion tons and may be more than 150 billion tons. At present prices, these amounts of oil, when recovered, would be worth from $250 billion to more than $3500 billion. Sixteen percent of world production of oil and gas already comes out of submarine wells, and drilling rigs are operating from the North Sea to the shores of Australia, and from West Africa to Alaska's Cook Inlet. About seventy-five nations are searching for off-shore oil, and production is underway or about to begin in twenty-four others. All this production comes from depths of less than 300 feet, but the technology is rapidly advancing, and drilling in depths from 600 feet to a mile of water will soon become possible.

These technological developments have raised an international political problem of the first magnitude. By accepted international convention, each coastal state has jurisdiction over exploration and recovery of the resources of the "seabed and subsoil" out to the edge of the continental shelf off its shores. But where is the edge? The question is relatively easy to answer when, as in the case of the North Sea, shallow water extends all the way from one coastal nation to another. The median line between two nations marks the limit of jurisdiction of each. In most places, however, the nations and their bordering shelves are separated by wide and deep ocean basins. The convention provides that the shelf extends out and down to the depths where exploitation is possible. Because it is likely that technology will soon be available for economic recovery of minerals at the greatest ocean depths, it is not hard to imagine the nations extending their claims out to the midline of the ocean basins that separate them, and thus attempting to establish sovereignty over areas vastly larger than their own land areas. The position is somewhat similar to that which existed before the Northwest Ordinance of 1787, when some of the former Thirteen Colonies declared that their boundaries extended between two parallel lines across the continent from the Atlantic to the Pacific.

Beside the obvious threat to the principle of *res communis,* there are two other uncomfortable aspects of this situation. Some former colonial powers, notably France and Britain, have kept possession of small islands throughout the world ocean; under the present convention, the "shelves" off these islands could be taken to extend for thousands of miles in several directions, to the median lines separating them from the continents. Elsewhere, small, sparsely populated coastal states can claim jurisdiction over very large areas. By leasing exploration and exploitation rights to corporations from the advanced nations, they may obtain huge royalties that will be used, if past experience with Saudi Arabia and such "ministates" as Kuwait, Bahrein, and the sultanates of Trucial

Oman is a guide, largely for military hardware and conspicuous consumption by a small elite.

In the near future, the problem is likely to be most serious for the continental slope at depths from 600 to more than 6,000 feet. Off Africa, the slope covers a greater area than the continental shelf, though, on a world-wide basis, it is somewhat narrower than the shelf. An apparently rich and extensive deposit of metallic sulfide ores has been discovered recently in a mile-deep depression in the Red Sea about half way between Saudi Arabia and Ethiopia. Under what legal arrangements should it be exploited? Over a longer time horizon, deep salt-domes of the Gulf of Mexico (which probably contain sulfur and petroleum deposits) and the cobalt-, copper-, and nickel-rich manganese nodules of the deep-sea floor may be of real concern.

Use of Resources Poses Problems

The problem of the "shelves" off oceanic islands can probably be solved by accommodation among the great powers, but the question of the optimum use of the resources of the continental slopes and the deep-sea floor is a far more difficult one that may take several decades to resolve. If the less-developed nations are to gain much real benefit from these resources, it may be necessary to place them under the jurisdiction of an international agency that could grant exclusive licenses for exploration and exploitation in return for a share of the proceeds. Such an agency would need to be able to take decisive action in accordance with principles of economics and equity, and with due regard to the major interests involved, but without the international logrolling that stultifies many existing United Nations organizations. It should probably be newly created within the United Nations family. Perhaps it could best be governed by a board of directors representing major continental areas, rather than individual nations.

A new "International Ocean Agency" might gradually assume five other functions: conservation of high-seas fisheries; establishment of regulations to prevent pollution by tankers and other ships at sea; surveillance of nuclear submarines; promotion of international cooperation in oceanography; and equitable control of large-scale modifications of ocean weather.

By the beginning of the 21st century, it may be possible to increase the harvest of ocean fish and other animals fourfold, from about 50 million tons gathered at present to 200 million tons, if present annual rates of growth can be maintained. This may require major advances in fisheries technology aimed at harvesting and processing many varieties of small fish that are not now taken, plus the "krill," or large planktonic crustacea of the Antarctic Ocean, that were the principal food of whales before these giant animals were virtually exterminated by a ruthless and short-sighted fishery. To sustain such a large catch will certainly require more effective international regulation of fishing industries than has been possible under present arrangements. To ensure economic returns and technological advances, these regulations may need to include control of entry into different fisheries, as well as catch limitations. The history of the whaling industry since World War II is a sorry example of the in-effectiveness of present international arrangements. Because the International Whaling Commission had no real authority, and could operate only by securing unanimous agreement among its member nations, it was impossible to limit the catch of any one species, but only, instead, the total weight taken from all species hunted by the fishery. The result was that the largest, and therefore most desirable, species was almost elimi-nated before the whalers turned their attention to the next largest, and so on through each of the species involved. Now, the numbers of all species have been driven down to such a low level that the prospects of recovery of the populations within the next fifty years is tragically slight.

Mariculture — The Farming of the Future

Part of the anticipated increase in the marine harvest will come from ocean farming, primarily in estuaries and other near-shore areas. The Japanese have already had considerable success in growing oysters, and have made a beginning with shrimps and other crustaceans. In oyster farming, they have managed to increase the productivity of an acre of marine land from twenty-five- to fifty-fold, from around 500 pounds of animal tissue per acre to between 15,000 and 30,000 pounds. One of the keys to this success has been their practice of attaching the oysters to long ropes hanging from buoys, both to avoid predators and to use the entire volume of the ocean and not just the bottom. Using somewhat similar techniques, Italian mussel farmers have obtained yields of hundreds of tons per acre.

These results suggest that we need to think of mariculture in quite a different way than agriculture. In modern farming on land, large quantities of chemical fertilizers are added to the soil, and plant crops use these nutrients. In the case of marine farming, the ocean can provide not chemical fertilizer for plants but food for animals, that is, the plankton — tiny floating plants and animals — the animals we want to harvest feed upon. This means that the areas most useful for mariculture are not those that can be enclosed or fenced in and fertilized with chemicals, but rather those in which there is a continual through-put of plankton carried by tidal and other inshore currents past the locality where the animal crop is being grown.

Although mariculture will undoubtedly grow in importance in the future, particularly if it can be mechanized, the large-scale development of the living resources of the sea will probably depend to a much greater extent on range or pasture management, of somewhat the same kind as now practiced over many land areas in raising cattle and sheep. In the pastures of the sea, we should harvest a balanced catch of different fish species at the same ecological level and control the populations of un-usable species, just as the manager of a livestock range tries to make sure that the cattle graze on both wanted and unwanted plants and controls the population of other animals that compete with the cattle for food. Control of predators is desirable in both land and sea pastures, as is improvement of the breeds of cattle and of such self-corralling fishes as salmon and other anadromous species. Both kinds of pastures may be made more productive by spraying them with relatively small quantities of minor nutrients, such as cobalt-containing compounds. In the ocean pastures, we may be able eventually to increase plankton production and, hence, the fishes' food supply, by changing circulation patterns or speeding up the vertical interchange of surface water and deep nutrient-containing water.

Pollution Increases Foreseen

As recent accidents have shown, the likelihood of widespread pollution of the sea surface and beaches by the wrecking of the new large tankers is rapidly increasing with the growth of ocean oil transport. These new sources add to the old problem of pollution from the fuel tanks of ordinary cargo vessels.

To prevent tanker pollution, it may be necessary to prescribe the routes and destinations of these monster vessels, and to insist that they load and unload by means of underwater pipelines at a considerable distance from land. Special navigational facilities and means for monitoring their passage at all points, similar to those used for airplanes over the United States, may be required, and these could well be administered by the proposed International Ocean Agency. An alternative would be to abandon tankers altogether, and to transport oil through pipelines installed on the sea floor across the ocean basins. Some rough cost calculations indicate that such pipelines could be economically competitive with the largest present tankers.

Undersea 'Radar Network'

Nuclear-powered missile-launching submarines are today a major component of the deterrent forces that maintain the balance of terror between the Soviet Union and the United States. Because of their mobility and invisibility, they have the great advantage that "first-strike" or "counterforce" weapons cannot be used effectively against them, and hence their response in a nuclear confrontation can be both delayed and measured. Thus, in a sense, they have much positive value in peacekeeping between the two superpowers.

But the seemingly inevitable proliferation of atomic weapons will almost certainly be accompanied by a similar proliferation of nuclear submarines. When many nations possess both these objects, submarine mobility and invisibility will change from a dubious blessing into an undoubted nightmare. The possibilities of international mischief-making by a smaller power deploying its submarines in distant waters are unpleasant to think about. One possible solution may be the establishment of an international surveillance system consisting of a network of underwater sound devices, possibly augmented by lasers, which would detect, identify, and track all large submerged vehicles at all times, much as objects in outer space are tracked today. This process of making the ocean "transparent" could well be one of the prime functions of the International Ocean Agency.

An Unlimited Horizon in Technology

Oceanography can be defined in various ways: as the scientific study of the part of the earth that is covered by seawater, or, more broadly, as those activities within the ocean that have significant scientific or technological content.

A host of new instruments and new methods are on the horizon that could lead to an explosive growth in oceanography during the next several decades. Among these are: computers to investigate complex hydrodynamic models and to handle large quantities of data; worldwide navigational systems using satellites and ground-based radio stations that allow a ship almost anywhere to locate itself within a few hundred feet; new submersible vehicles of various kinds; the so-called man-in-the-sea programs, started by the French and now being vigorously pursued in the United States, which look forward to men living in the ocean for extended periods — going down even to great depths in the sea and staying there for weeks or months on end; the possibility of anchoring a network of instrumented buoys in mid-ocean that will make continuous observations over extended periods; the use of satellites to study the near-surface waters and the overlying atmospheric cloud patterns; free-floating and bottom-mounted instruments; the many scientific uses of underwater sound and the possible use of lasers to multiply the distance at which underwater objects can be seen, and, most exciting of all to geologists, the possibility of drilling and sampling the entire column of sea-floor sediments and the underlying rocks.

Cooperation Among Nations Needed

Just as all men breathe the same air, and a storm over New England may have begun off Japan, so the ocean waters are indivisible, and events in one part of the sea eventually have effects at great distances. Oceanography is thus not only a natural field of international scientific cooperation, but also such cooperation is necessary if human understanding of the oceans is to keep pace with human needs. Only in this way can the knowledge required for improvements in long-range weather forecasting, development of ocean fisheries on a worldwide basis, better routing of merchant vessels, greater national security, and rational solutions of international controversies about ocean resources be obtained at a minimum cost to all interested nations.

Many marine problems demand international cooperation for their effective investigation, particularly in cases where:

¶ The scale of research is greater than can be mobilized by any one of the nations concerned.

¶ The research involves a greater diversity of scientific competence or facilities than possessed by any one of the interested nations.

¶ Solution of a problem requires access to data and experience possessed

172

by several nations (for example, the assessment of the condition of a fish stock exploited by many nations requires the pooling of information).

¶ The cost-effectiveness of the research for each nation can be substantially increased by joining forces in an international operation (this is the case in nearly all multiship international investigations).

¶ The subject of research is affected by activities or laws of another nation (for example, many interesting geological features of the sea floor extend offshore from the coasts of different countries across the continental shelf).

¶ There is special need to reach agreement on the employment of comparable methods of research (an ocean-wide study of primary organic production by standard methods could probably be accomplished only through international cooperation).

¶ There is a need to establish mutual confidence in observations or analyses bearing on particular problems of international action (for example, when stock assessments have revealed a need for regulation of exploitation, as in the case of Antarctic whales, appraisal of the effects of alternative regulations requires joint analysis of biological statistics by scientists serving in an international capacity).

Among the most obvious reasons for international oceanographic cooperation is the need for taking censuses of fish populations in the world ocean. No one really knows how many fish there are in the sea, nor how rapidly they can reproduce themselves.

Some species of fishes and invertebrates of the high seas wander over great distances, and their distribution and abundance change with changes in the oceanic environment. To find the sizes, distribution, and interrelationships of these populations is important to the rapid development, and indispensable for the conservation, of world fisheries.

A second area where international cooperation is essential is in the making of systematic surveys of the shape of the deep-sea floor. At present, our maps of the deep ocean are about equal in accuracy and detail to the maps of the land published 200 years ago. The task of making ocean maps will require the continuous operation over several decades of a dozen or more specially equipped vessels, and an international navigation network. If this great task can be shared among all interested nations, the expenses to any one nation will not be burdensome.

Weather Forecasting Can Be Improved

Recent meteorological studies show that changes in world weather patterns over periods of weeks to many years are closely related to changes in the temperature of the ocean waters. Because the sea behaves more sluggishly than the air, studies of these changes may make it possible to improve the accuracy of long-range weather forecasts. The present accuracy is low, but if it could be increased, great economic benefits would follow — for example, in planting and harvesting crops, in planning seasonal fuel transportation and storage, in the timing of building and road construction, and in flood and drought protection. In the United States alone, a real improvement in the accuracy of long-range weather forecasting could produce savings of billions of dollars every year.

Measurements at numerous points over vast areas are required to study the changes in the sea and the air. At the present time, no nation by itself has enough research ships or oceanographers to make all the needed measurements. Cooperation among oceanographers and meteorologists of different nations is essential.

The Sea Will Become a Playground

One of the most important uses of the ocean in the future will be for recreation. Much of this will be in the near-shore zone. In many parts of the world the shoreline needs to be stretched, or "wrinkled," in order to make it much longer than at present. This could be done by building peninsulas and offshore bars and islands, and by dredging estuaries and bays. But our knowledge of the oceanic processes that stabilize shorelines is still far from adequate to allow us to build and maintain such structures inexpensively and effectively.

The development of small submarines for recreational, scientific, and engineering purposes, and the man-in-the-sea programs are liable to change our very attitude toward the ocean. We human beings are land animals, even though the salt in our blood tells us that our remote ancestors were sea creatures. The sea surface has always been a nearly impenetrable curtain for us, whether we were on a ship at sea or looking at the wavy surface of the ocean from the beach. The new capacity to move and live under water will give us new insights and new interests — a feeling of being at home in the great volume of the ocean, and a capacity for thinking about the interior of the sea as a place for man.

Unlike space exploration, which can be indulged in only by a few men with enormous resources at their disposal, the voyage to inner space may turn out to be comparatively inexpensive. Before the turn of the century, it may be possible for anyone with about $5,000 to have his own submarine, which will go down to depths of several miles. There may be hordes of moderately well-to-do amateurs in small submersibles — perhaps getting in the way of scientific submarines; perhaps making new discoveries on their own; certainly getting into trouble at various times; in any case requiring many new developments of undersea technology to take care of them.

Advances in Marine Sciences

Because the oceans are so vast and so little known, almost any nation that borders on the sea can make important contributions to oceanography, even with a modest effort. Oceanography deals with a familiar and visible, yet mysterious, part of the real world, consequently it is an easily understood kind of science, well suited to creating public understanding of the purposes and methods of scientific research. At the same time, the less developed nations need to learn a great deal about their bordering seas, as a basis for conservation and full development of their fisheries, and for many other purposes. But many of these nations are too small or too poor to be able to afford a sufficiently broad and strong oceanographic institution. Through the mechanisms of international collaboration, the oceanographic institutions of the rich nations can provide facilities and intellectual back-up to the scientists in the poor nations and work with them on their national problems.

International scientific cooperation in the marine sciences would be greatly strengthened by the creation of an effective and adequately budgeted international oceanographic organization on a worldwide scale. Because ocean science and technology, like agricultural research, must be mainly supported by governments, the basic international oceanographic organization should be intergovernmental, and, consequently, the proposed new International Ocean Agency might assume responsibility for planning and coordinating oceanographic cooperation as one of its functions.

In its scientific activities it would need a counterpart controlled by scientists and speaking with the voice of science rather than of governments. This might take the form of an international union of marine sciences, which could be one of the constituent Unions of the International Council of Scientific Unions. Two of its purposes would be to help marine scientists talk to each other through scientific meetings and publications and to develop the scientific infrastructure of standards, nomenclature, bibliographies, information exchange, and intercalibration of methods. But it would have another, more important objective, and that would be to exert an influence for scientific integrity and imaginative change on the International Ocean Agency. Like the players in "Hamlet," the principal task of a private world organization of oceanographers would be "to catch the conscience of the King."

We need to think about more than observation and measurement, or theory and understanding, or even forecasting and prediction. What can be done to control or change the ocean? There are many possibilities for both small- and large-scale changes.

Off the coast of California, most of the water is too cold to swim in. It may be possible to warm it up, particularly in the near-shore zone, by using waste heat from the large nuclear power plants of the future — plants that will generate many thousand megawatts of power. If a way could be found to keep a 200-meter-wide ribbon of water near the beach warm enough for comfort, the new recreational areas that could be developed might be worth a good many millions of dollars.

A first-order change might be brought about by spreading thin particles of reflecting materials near the sea surface in the areas of generation of tropical storms or hurricanes, in such a way as to prevent overheating, during the summer time, of the waters near the surface in these areas. There might be two consequences, one favorable and one unfavorable: (1) hurricanes might be prevented from forming, and (2) there might be a sharp decrease in rainfall over large land areas. Another possibility of the same kind, in reverse, would be to decrease the reflectivity of the earth and thereby increase solar heating by spreading a thin powder of nonreflecting materials over ice- or snow-covered areas. The potentialities for spreading small amounts of light-reflecting or absorbing materials over large regions will probably be considerably greater in the future.

These potentialities should be exploited with great caution, and only after we have gained much more understanding than we now possess of oceanic and atmospheric processes, so that we can predict all the probable consequences of our actions. Even under the best of circumstances, however, there are liable to be both favorable and unfavorable effects. Some people will be benefited and others will be worse off than they would have been if the natural processes had not been modified. The possibility of stopping hurricane formation, described above, is an example. Many lives might be saved and much property damage prevented, but the reduction in rainfall might bring serious losses to farmers. Here the International Ocean Agency might find its most important task — to make sure that the real benefits from ocean weather modification significantly exceed the real costs, and to arrange means for compensating those individuals and groups who suffer losses.